REBIRTHING
and breathwork

CATHERINE DOWLING

REBIRTHING
and breathwork

*A powerful technique
for personal transformation*

PIATKUS

All case histories in this book are included with permission, and all names and life circumstances have been changed to protect confidentiality

Published in 2000 by
Judy Piatkus (Publishers) Limited
5 Windmill Street
London W1P 1HF
e-mail: info@piatkus.co.uk

For the latest news and information on all our titles,
visit our website at www.piatkus.co.uk

A catalogue record for this book is available from the British Library

ISBN 0 7499 2092 0

Edited by Anne Lawrance

Set by Phoenix Photosetting, Chatham, Kent

Printed and bound in Great Britain by
www.biddles.co.uk

Contents

v

Introduction

'Breath is our companion – on our travels to deep levels and
wide horizons of consciousness – in search of the true self.'
[Wilfried Ehrmann, Ph. D., *Breath is Your Companion*]

Rebirthing is a breathing technique. It is very simple to learn and
comes quite easily and naturally to the vast majority of the people
who use it. But its simplicity is deceptive. If you were to watch
someone rebirthing, you might see their chest moving, sometimes
quickly, sometimes slowly, sometimes hardly moving at all. You
might see them shift about, yawn, scratch. There might be some
crying, sometimes quite a lot of crying. There might also be some
laughter. And, at the end of the session, you might see someone
so deeply relaxed that they haven't a tense muscle in their body.
You might also notice radiant skin, luminous eyes and a face that,
at least for a time, looks years younger than when they lay down
to begin the breathing session just an hour earlier.

But nothing you can see would give you any indication of the
depth and wonder of the world you can't see, the world rebirthing
opens up inside the person who is breathing. Sometimes that world
is experienced physically. The rebirthee may feel tingling in their
hands or feet, changes in their body temperature or localised pain.
They may experience waves of energy moving upwards, gathering
in intensity until they come cascading back downwards after

1

reaching the head. The rebirthee may see fabulous swirling colours, hear sounds, experience deep relaxation or feel their whole body vibrate with aliveness and vitality.

That world also contains memories from the distant and not-so-distant past, memories that have been forgotten and ones that have never been forgotten. These memories are more real than anything we normally recall because in rebirthing they are multi-dimensional. In other words, it is more like reliving than remembering. Although the memories can be very real, the rebirthee always knows where he or she is – lying down in their rebirther's consulting room. This is because, while rebirthing, linear time disappears. We can be deep in the past and fully in the present all at once. And sometimes rebirthees describe what they experience as coming from another lifetime, a previous incarnation.

The inner world is emotional. The rebirthee can feel intense joy and intense sadness. They can feel fear, anger, the pain of loss or abandonment, sorrow, disgust . . . And then, as they keep breathing, those emotions fade away. They become integrated, worked through, relegated to their rightful place within the breather. But there are also other emotions: joy, contentment, peace, or satisfaction so intense it is physical as well as emotional. The end result is a growing sense of lightness, freedom and well-being.

There is also a place for the mind. In the same way as our sense of time dissolves into something more fluid, the usual limitations to our thinking also fade away. We cease to think in the forms and structures of everyday life and the result can be very valuable and profound insights into ourselves, others and life itself. These insights are like little epiphanies, moments of real and lasting change and from them life can flow more creatively.

Rebirthing is a journey inwards into the past. It is often about revisiting birth. Birth is a deeply formative experience which can lay down patterns of behaviour so strong they affect every aspect of our life. Revisiting birth through rebirthing can help dissolve these old patterns. But birth memories don't arise for everyone. This is because rebirthing is much more than revisiting birth. Rebirthing is also about resolving the many layers of past experience most people carry around with them. And as these layers fall away, the rebirthee can feel reborn in a much broader sense. Then rebirthing becomes a journey outwards – a journey into the world, claiming a place within it, living creatively. It is a journey towards connection, towards a feeling of belonging, not just or necessarily with people, but within the grand scheme of things, the ecosystem or however each person defines what has traditionally been called creation.

Rebirthing is a healing technique, but in rebirthing healing is not just the product of arriving at some form of understanding and intellectual clarity. It is not simply the cathartic release of emotion and it is not only the dissolving of energy blocks in the body. Rebirthing is all of these things. The mind, the body, the emotions and the spirit are all engaged at once in a world where time and normal limitations of thought, feeling and the senses dissolve into a flowing, uplifting experience of regeneration. Because of this, healing through rebirthing is deep and profound. It is experienced with the whole of one's being rather than at just one level of exist-ence. Rebirthing is the difference between believing and really knowing something, between dipping your toe in the water and actually swimming, between thinking about eating a slice of cake and seeing, touching, smelling and actually eating it.

A Personal Experience

I began training as a rebirther about eight years ago. Rebirthers learn a lot from their clients, so every so often I review my client case histories to see if any relevant patterns are emerging. One particular group of clients, mostly women in their late twenties and early thirties, when asked why they wanted to do rebirthing, gave almost word for word, the same answer: 'I don't know who I am and I don't know what I want'. And that was exactly the point in my own life at which I came to rebirthing.

3

I had just returned home after several years in the United States where I had been busy developing an ulcer and chronic back pain from the stress of teaching in a New York City high school. As a child I had many ambitions, most of them secret. I wanted to write books and to find a job I would love and which would make me want to go to work in the morning. I was told many times that such a job didn't exist and as for the writing, in the depressed Ireland of the 1960s and '70s, book contracts were the prerogative of other people, not me. So instead I trained as a teacher. It was a nice, secure, respectable job helping people and doing good in the world. But the first time I set foot in a classroom as a teacher I knew that I was in the wrong job.

Most of my clients who identify their problems as not knowing who they are, also have good jobs they don't like and sometimes even hate. They stick with those jobs for the same reason I stayed with teaching for so long – it was something I 'should' do. The word should is very important. For many people it becomes a kind of tyranny. I *should* stay in a job that is leading me to a nervous breakdown because it is all about helping others and I *should* help others, or because it pays well and at my age I *should* be earning lots of money. I *should* solve people's problems for them, feel bad when my partner feels bad, phone someone I have no desire to talk to, keep my mouth shut when I am bursting to express opinions that others won't like, say 'yes' when I mean 'no' . . . The list is endless. I have found for myself and my clients that the word 'should' can be a gateway into the past and to what is troubling them most. For example, when a child moulds themselves to the needs of others, they tend to lose sight of themselves. They begin to forget what their own needs are and soon they are making choices and decisions based on what they should do rather than what they want. The result can be a deeply unhappy child. As an adult the wrong career choice or a bad relationship can simply be the visible face of issues that run very deep. Beneath the surface can lurk depression, the loneliness of never connecting honestly

4

with another person, shyness and the feeling of suffocation that comes from walking around imprisoned behind a facade from which there seems to be no escape.

For me, the necessity of finding a new career was the catalyst that set off a series of coincidences that fall into the category of what Carl Jung called 'synchronicity'.* I could do something about a career, the rest I was stuck with for life. But the new career and the new way of being began one evening on a bus.

I was coming home from yet another failed interview when a woman I hadn't seen in nearly twenty years boarded the bus. She was embarking on a new career that combined traditional health practices with complementary therapy. I had never heard of complementary therapy. She suggested she and I go out to dinner with her cousin whom I had known in secondary school and gave me her phone number. I promptly lost it. About a year later, while clearing out some boxes, I came across the tiny piece of paper with her phone number on it and within a week all three of us were sitting in a restaurant in Dublin talking about rebirthing. My friend from school had become a rebirther. Listening to them talk I thought they were both totally bonkers. Of course I couldn't possibly rock the boat by saying this, so I just listened and nodded in what I thought were the right places. But one thing I couldn't deny was that my old school friend was a very much happier and younger looking woman than the one I had last seen over 10 years ago.

Some time later another friend heard a rebirther trainer called Stephen Gregory speaking about rebirthing on a radio show that he normally never listens to. There was a rebirther training course coming up and my friend suggested I go to the introductory talk. We both went. Steve was an excellent speaker. I can't remember the exact details of what he said, but what I heard was that this breathing technique offered me the chance to escape from some-

* For an exploration of Jung's theories, see Jung, C.J., *Memories, Dreams, Reflections* (ed Jaffe, A.), London, Fontana, 1995.

thing I believed I would just have to live with for life. In the light of this, career opportunities became irrelevant. It was something I wanted to do for myself.

Before being accepted for the course I had to do a rebirthing session. I told my rebirther that I didn't really have any problems, I just wasn't fulfilling my potential. She got me to lie down and begin the breathing technique and it was one of the most physically painful experiences I have ever had. Every joint in my body locked in tetany (see p. 129) and I could feel something terrifying and heavy pressing down on top of me. In hindsight I would say it was the memory of a very difficult birth but at the time all I knew was that this technique *worked*. I realised that training in rebirthing was the right thing for me to do.

During my training I came to understand that rebirthing is about freedom. It is a fast and amazingly effective way of liberating our core selves from inner constraints, from the tyranny of 'should', from the strait-jacket of a lifetime of conditioning. The result is a life lived creatively, a life lived in daily contact with who we are, not who we think we should be.

So what of childhood dreams? I have had about twenty-five jobs in my life. The only one I enjoyed was waitressing but the enjoyment wore off after about six months. Now I have achieved my diploma from the Association of Irish Rebirthers and I work as a rebirther. I have a steady stream of clients and I look forward to every session and find every person's story fascinating. I also co-ordinate a two-year professional rebirther training programme which is facilitated by Stephen Gregory and accredited by the Open College Network. But what has surprised me most is that I have been able to do something I never thought I was capable of – public speaking. Now I give lectures, run courses in personal development, chair committees and speak at conferences – all things I would have once found impossible. This discovery of hidden talents, abilities and interests is something I have seen again and again in clients and it never ceases to amaze them.

Who Does Rebirthing?

Rebirthing is a journey towards freedom. But the obstacles to freedom are many and varied and it is these obstacles that propel people into seeking therapy through rebirthing. They include:

- relationship difficulties or patterns that keep repeating themselves in every relationship;
- not knowing who you are or what you want;
- not living up to your potential;
- feeling trapped in a way of being, stressed out by efforts to please others;
- stress;
- job-related problems;
- depression;
- anxiety, panic attacks, phobias;
- shyness and low self-esteem, lack of confidence;
- general unhappiness with what seems like every aspect of your life;
- an inability to feel;
- abuse;
- simply wanting to get to know yourself better and enjoy life more.

This list is not exhaustive. People come for all sorts of reasons and rebirthing addresses all these issues and more. But it is important to remember that rebirthing isn't just or all about resolving problems. It is also about feeling more alive, free and in touch with the self.

How to Use this Book

This book is written as an introduction to rebirthing. But just as rebirthing is about a journey inwards, this book is also designed to assist you in your own inner journey whether or not you decide to take rebirthing sessions as a result of reading it. Because rebirthing is an experience, it is impossible to condense it into a set of instructions as you would for a purely mechanical technique. This book is not intended as a manual from which you can learn to rebirth yourself. I have included a short breathing exercise which will give you a flavour of the rebirthing method of breathing, but if you intend to do rebirthing, begin rebirthing by taking sessions with a trained rebirther. It usually doesn't take long for clients to learn how to use their breath to rebirth themselves, but it is best to begin with a professional rebirther.

However, this book does contain exercises that I use, sometimes with clients, but mostly in my personal-development classes. They are designed to help you begin to explore your inner world. They can help you test the waters of self-development or they can lead you deep into your own explorations. If you find they stir up deep emotions that you feel uncomfortable handling, stop, use the third breathing exercise from chapter 2 (see p. 26) and seek out a professional rebirther.

In Part 1 of this book we will look at the origins of the breathing technique known as rebirthing and its place within the long tradition of breathwork. You will learn the basics of breathing, how it affects your health and well-being and how rebirthing can provide a gentle and very effective way of exploring your inner self.

Part 2 focuses on how human beings are affected by life, become damaged, are conditioned by what they experience from womb time to the present. Each chapter is followed by personal development exercises that can help you identify your own conditioning, your own issues.

And in Part 3 we will look in detail at how to free yourself from that conditioning through rebirthing, insight and self-acceptance. There are also suggestions for breathing exercises to use at home and how to use rebirthing to develop your creativity and manage the stress in your life.

PART 1

THE BASICS

1

✥

In the Beginning

The 1950s in the United States saw a major shift in responsibility for the care and development of people's mental and emotional health. Therapy was, in many respects, moving out of the hands of psychiatrists and psychiatric institutions and into the homes of ordinary people. The decade saw the rise of a variety of personal-growth groups which were given the umbrella title of encounter groups. These were groups of ordinary people interested in their own mental and emotional development who met regularly to follow a programme of personal growth. They were the forerunners of present-day personal-development groups and at the time were sometimes referred to as 'group therapy for normals'.[1] This popular movement continued in the 1960s and expanded rapidly in the nurturing atmosphere of flower power and popular revolt that characterised that decade.

At the same time, in the world of psychiatry, the practice of working with altered states of consciousness was fairly well established by the 1960s. Sandoz Pharmaceuticals in Switzerland had developed a drug called Lysergic Acid or LSD in 1943. The company sent supplies of the chemical to select mental-health institutions throughout the world and psychiatrists began to use it in the treatment of patients. In 1955 two psychologists at Kaiser hospital in Oakland, California conducted a nine-month study of patients undergoing conventional psychotherapy, comparing them with a group of people on the waiting list for psychotherapy at the hospital. At the end of nine months they found that the results for both groups was largely the same: one third improved, one third stayed the same, one third deteriorated. Leary and Barron, the psychologists involved in the study, drew the conclusion not that psychotherapy was ineffective, but that the collection of techniques involved in psychotherapy sometimes worked and sometimes didn't. When therapy did work, something else, a 'vitalising trans-action' was occurring. This Barron described as 'ephemeral, as frail as love or blessedness . . .'[2] These vitalising transactions took place beyond the limits of ordinary awareness, in non-ordinary states of consciousness. In other words, deep, significant and last-ing mental and emotional healing took place when the patient was able to look upon the world and their own internal process from a perspective he or she would not normally experience.

The publication of Leary and Barron's findings caused a stir in the mental-health profession and gave credence to the use of a drug which induced just such non-ordinary states of consciousness. Timothy Leary went on to become one of the leading advocates of LSD therapy and a guru of the drug culture of the era. Other famous advocates of the therapeutic effects of the drug were the Beatnik poets, the writers Aldous Huxley, Ken Keasy and Anais Nin and the actor Cary Grant who once described the experience as being 'born again'.[3] However, at the same time as people were touting the very real therapeutic effects of LSD therapy, others such as Anais Nin began to point out the equally real dangers of the drug. One psychiatrist working with LSD was Stanislav Grof. Grof began to notice that his patients experienced an alteration of their breathing patterns while undergoing LSD therapy. He began to experiment with this breathing pattern and eventually he and his wife developed the breathing technique they called holotropic breathing. The breathwork practice which included the use of music and loud sounds could bring about the altered state of consciousness deemed to be the therapeutic factor in the drug therapy.

These then were the two broad trends that formed the background to the discovery of the breathing technique known as rebirthing. Rebirthing was developed in the United States in the late 1960s and early '70s by Leonard Orr. Orr was one of the many ordinary people throughout the '60s who experimented with various and often unorthodox methods of personal growth, and with the phenomenon of altered states of consciousness. He spent many years searching for self-development techniques and his search involved subjecting himself to a variety of experiences such as long hours in a sauna or in hot or cold baths. Once he pushed past what he called the '"urgency barrier", the mechanism that keeps us from going too deep into ourselves,'[4] he achieved the altered state of consciousness that allowed deep and profound insights and memories to surface. In his work on himself and other people he made a similar discovery to Stanislav Grof, and, like Grof, he began to experiment with using the breath to bring about the same altered states. It worked, and Orr developed the breathing technique he called rebirthing.

Beyond the Bath

The name rebirthing seemed appropriate because many of Orr's experiences with the technique were birth related and he noticed a similar pattern when using the technique with friends and acquaintances. But as we've already seen, rebirthing is much more than revisiting birth and Orr's students took the practice of rebirthing well beyond the original hot bath. One of the first to do this was Sondra Ray. She developed a seminar based on the conclusions that she and Orr had drawn from their client work and used the technique itself as part of the seminar. Fairly quickly the Loving Relationships Training or LRT expanded beyond the actual seminar and grew into an organisation which also ran professional rebirther training courses and registered rebirthers internationally. Around the same time two other well-known rebirthers, Jim Leonard and Phil Laut, developed their own form of rebirthing called Vivation which has also gained prominence world-wide. In 1995 the LRT was dissolved and replaced by the Association of Rebirther Trainers International (ARTI) which continues to run rebirther training programmes and register rebirthers.

At the same time as Ray and others were developing the LRT form of rebirthing, rebirthers in various countries around the world began to organise themselves into national registration and networking bodies (see Useful Addresses p. 178) and many other schools of rebirthing grew out of the work of individual practitioners. These schools, ARTI included, can vary greatly in their approach to rebirthing and prospective rebirthees might find some more suited to their needs and temperament than others. In 1994, seeing the need to organise and network internationally, rebirthers and other breathworkers from places as diverse as South America, Russia, Australia, the United States and various European countries came together to form the International Breathwork Foundation (IBF). The IBF promotes research into breathwork and related topics and publishes an international directory of breathworkers as well as hosting the annual Global Inspiration Conference. This conference provides a platform for the latest research into breathwork as well as generating recommendations for effectiveness, professionalism, ethics and integrity in breathwork practice. Through the work of the IBF and various national bodies, rebirthing is gaining acceptance world-wide as a legitimate tool of psychotherapy – although the technique is far more than a form of psychotherapy. Rebirthing is also gaining academic recognition and rebirther training programmes in Ireland, the UK, Australia and elsewhere are beginning to access mainstream nationally recognised accreditation.

Eastern Roots

The use of breathing to promote mental and physical health as well as spiritual growth is not new. Rebirthing is one of many forms of breathwork and there are many parallels in Eastern practices. While schools of breathwork existed in ancient Egypt, Greece and Rome, often as part of the medical systems of those cultures, it is in the widely used breathing practices of China and India that the clearest links with rebirthing are found. There is no direct lineage between these practices and rebirthing as developed by Orr but the similarities are clear. In China, the Qi Gong system contained a wide range of movement and breathing techniques designed to promote different aspects of mental, physical and spiritual well-being. The techniques vary. Some involve fast breathing, others slow. Sometimes breathing is through the nose, sometimes through the mouth and occasionally it is in through one and out through the other. Each technique has its own physical, psychological and/or spiritual purpose. Some are used to develop calmness, others to raise self-esteem, bring about changes in body functions, promote spiritual awareness or to effect countless other phenomena. In common with modern breathwork specialists, the ancient Chinese associated shallow, fast breathing with anxiety and worry and connected upper-chest breathing with feelings of love and harmony with people, life and nature, an effect familiar to most people who have experienced rebirthing. For a more detailed account of the ancient Chinese practices, read Gunnel Minett's book *Breath and Spirit* (see Selected Reading).

The other great breathwork tradition to influence Western practices is yoga. Hatha yoga uses physical exercises and postures to cleanse body, mind and soul. Fundamental to the practice of yoga are the breathing techniques known as pranayama. The breath, among other things, is the vehicle for prana, the life force, and the breath and prana are inseparable. To breathe in air is to breathe in energy. This is something Leonard Orr has talked about and, sooner or later, something most rebirthees experience. As personal psychological issues are resolved through rebirthing, rebirthees begin to experience the breath as a vital connection with the life force and thus with the ecosystem of which they are a part. In this way, the rebirthing experience can take the rebirthee beyond birth and their personal history into the realm of the transpersonal, the spiritual dimension recognised in the West as a vital element of human consciousness by Carl Jung among others.

2

ॐ

Breathing

'Melancholoke folke are commonly given to sigh because the minde
being possessed by a great varietie and store of foolish apparitions
doth not remember or suffer the partie to be at leisure to
breathe according to the necessitie of nature.'
[Dulaurans, 1559]

Rebirthing is breathing. Breathing is the most vital of all the bodily
functions. We can survive for days without drinking, weeks, even
months without eating or excreting. We survive a matter of minutes
without breathing. Yet it is something most of us take for granted.
Until we develop asthma or emphysema or get a lungful of un-
wanted smoke we barely notice the fact that we are breathing every
minute of every day. We rarely consider that something we do so
automatically and unobtrusively could have potential far beyond
the simple intake of oxygen. But just as most scientists now agree
that the average person in the course of their daily life uses only a
fraction of their brain, most people who work with the breath know
that the same is true for breathing. We tap into only a modicum of
the potential inherent in the breathing process.

With the growing popularity of yoga and the rapid increase in
the number of people involved in stress management, most people
are now aware of the calming effects of certain types of breathing.
But this is only a fraction of the benefits to be derived from
breathwork. Ways of breathing are numerous and the advantages
equally diverse. Therefore, before understanding the kind of

breathing used in rebirthing, it is helpful to look broadly at the process of breathing itself both on the physical level and as a method of interaction with life.

The Physical Process of Breathing

The average person breathes approximately 20,000 times per day. This means that in one 24-hour period roughly one hundred square metres of our lung surface is exposed to approximately 8000 litres of air, and 17.5 litres of blood passing through our lungs carries the oxygen from that air to every cell in our bodies. That oxygen allows our cells to produce the energy they need to survive, maintain health, deal with the stresses of daily living, and regenerate themselves when they reach the end of their lifespan. But what is equally important and not so well known is that, on the return journey from the cells, our blood carries seventy per cent of the body's waste products for elimination through the lungs. If for no other reason than to remove the toxins from our system, it pays to breathe effectively. Yet the vast majority of people do not breathe as fully or as efficiently as they could for maximum *physical* well-being. It is no wonder then that the vast array of other benefits – mental, emotional and spiritual – to be derived from the management of the breathing process have been largely ignored, at least in the West.

Beyond the Physical

The way a person breathes speaks eloquently of their relationship with life. Breathing is our most vital and intimate connection with the world around us. It is the way we take the universe into every cell in our bodies. Each breath we breathe contains approximately ten sextillion atoms. Those atoms may have, at some time, been inhaled and exhaled by every one of the roughly six billion people on earth.[5] If we see the world as the manifestation of energy, then

18

breathing is our most vital means of connecting with that world and everyone in it. There are few quicker ways of walking a mile in another man's shoes than by matching the rhythm of his breathing. Breathe the same way as another person and you get to see the world at least partly through their eyes.

The reason for this is that one of the least noticed yet fundamental ways we adjust to the events of our life is by altering our breathing patterns. In times of great stress we often hold our breath. At other times we push air out of our bodies until the breathing mechanism itself begins to shut down and we are left gasping for air. In times of great fear when a flight or fight response is indicated we breathe rapidly. If we do not, often the mental clarity needed to guide our actions does not manifest itself and we are left paralysed, unable to scream, to run or to defend ourselves. Our breathing becomes agitated, often erratic, when we are angry. We have difficulty breathing at all when we are upset. And as children we often hold our breath and close our eyes to make ourselves invisible, a practice we continue into adulthood but with far less awareness of what we are doing. We gasp, sigh and hold our breath in response to different emotions and in times of great pleasure, and when we feel safe and secure, we breathe fully and freely.[6] This link between breathing and emotions first came to the attention of scientists in the 1930s when researchers concluded that anxiety was a 'respiratory neurosis' and discovered that 'stimulating the breathing could momentarily restore sanity in schizophrenic patients'.[7] By the 1950s breathing patterns associated with various psychological disorders had been documented.

Body armouring is a well-known concept first developed by the great pioneer of breathwork, Wilhelm Reich. The term describes the way our bodies shape themselves in response to repeated events in our life. If we tighten certain muscles in response to a particular situation, those muscles will respond in the same way when we encounter that situation again. If this happens frequently enough the response will be imprinted in the muscles and will become a characteristic feature of our posture, the way we move and the way we hold ourselves. The same is true for breathing. Shallow, erratic or halting breathing, over- or underbreathing, incomplete exhalation, or full, free breathing can all be the result of years of responding to life events through the alteration of the breathing process. These alterations take place as an instinctive way of holding life at bay and making it less painful. We can repress painful experiences, feelings or thought patterns through restricting our breathing patterns. But the process is indiscriminate. Restricting our experience of painful feelings also affects our capacity for pleasure. In addition, we lock those experiences, unresolved, into our bodies where they continue to influence us even from outside the range of our awareness.

Fortunately the reverse is also true. Breathing, ordinarily controlled automatically by the autonomic nervous system, is, for most people, the only organ function that is also governed by the central nervous system. This means that this vital function can be consciously controlled by us at will. This fact puts at our disposal one of the most effective healing systems available to human beings. Breathing offers us not only safe access to our unconscious, but through certain breathing techniques it also becomes the means of healing the hurts and traumas that may be stored there.

Breathing Therapeutically

Consciously adjusting the breathing process has far-reaching therapeutic effects physically, mentally and emotionally. To understand the effects of the breathing technique used in rebirthing, it is useful to look first at therapeutic breathing in general. For the purpose of describing breathing the lungs can be divided into three sections and the type of breathing labelled according to the section of the lungs which is the focus.

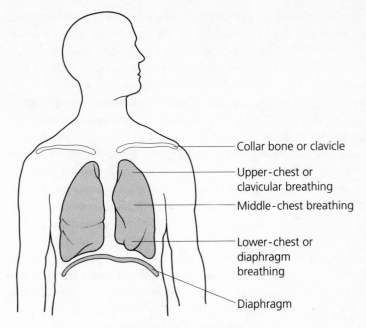

Collar bone or clavicle

Upper-chest or clavicular breathing

Middle-chest breathing

Lower-chest or diaphragm breathing

Diaphragm

Therapeutic Breathing

Diaphragm Breathing

Below the lungs is the powerful muscle known as the diaphragm. When the diaphragm is contracted it moves downwards into the abdomen and the effect in the lungs is to suck in air, or inhale. The inhaled air is then carried via the blood to every part of the body and some of the body's waste materials and carbon dioxide are carried back by the blood to the lungs. At this point the diaphragm relaxes. It moves back up into the chest cavity causing the lungs to exhale the waste materials which have accumulated there. Breathing into the lower chest is often known as diaphragm breathing and can be recognised by the characteristic swelling of the abdomen upon inhale. On a physical level this is probably the most efficient form of breathing because the area at the base of the lungs is the richest in blood supply. On a mental and emotional level diaphragm breathing can be practised consciously to bring about a state of deep relaxation and calm. It is the form of breathing used with most relaxation techniques, by singers and wind musicians to maximise the use of their lungs and by performers to calm nerves. But as in the holistic view of the person it is impossible to separate mind and body, this kind of breathing has a very interesting and dramatic dual effect. It makes the body heavier, more solid and better balanced (see exercises on pp. 25–27). This physical phenomenon can be very effective on a mental and emotional level in times of verbal aggression or heated, emotional argument when people don't always respect each other's boundaries. The breathing and physical solidity seem to act as a buffer against the sharpness of the attack, leaving the person under attack calm enough not to take offence. At the same time it keeps the breather grounded in their sense of self and in touch with their own thoughts and feelings. In other words their mind, informed by their feelings, remains clear enough to manage the situation.

Middle-chest Breathing

When the concentration of breathing is into the middle of the lungs, breathing is most likely to be shallow in comparison with diaphragm breathing. It is therefore the least efficient form of breathing for everyday activity. It is also the type of breathing most people do in the course of their ordinary daily lives.

Upper-chest or Clavicular Breathing

This is when the focus of the breath is in the upper portion of the lungs and is the type of breathing used in rebirthing. It is character-ised by a noticeable movement of the upper chest. While this form of breathing may cause some slight movement of the shoulders, there is no need to consciously move the shoulders while practising upper-chest breathing. To do so can cause unnecessary tension and take concentration away from the process of breathing. It is the form of breathing we use least and can be a little difficult to get used to if one is rigorously trained in diaphragm breathing. On a mental and emotional level, consciously breathing into this region can bring about great clarity of thought, access to unconscious material and a very deep level of emotional release. There is, as yet, little scientific research into the effects of rebirthing so I cannot provide a physiological explanation of why breathing allows access to the unconscious and at the same time provides the means of resolving the issues that surface as a result. A study is being conducted in co-operation with Wilfried Ehrmann of ATMAN and members of the Austrian Association for Professional Rebirthers and Breath Trainers in a hospital in Austria which may provide some answers, but it is still in the early stages. The degree of emotional release produced by clavicular breathing may be the reason why we unconsciously choose not to breathe into this area of our lungs.

Some Breathing Problems

Problems arise in the breathing mechanism ranging from serious conditions such as asthma to barely noticeable shallow breathing or incomplete breathing. Some conditions are worth mentioning here partly because they give a small flavour of the extent of breathing-related difficulties, and also because, in the past few years, they have come to the attention of medical and other professionals.

Hyperventilation or overbreathing is caused by too rapid, shallow chest breathing in which there is an emphasis on the exhale. Normally when we breathe the amount of oxygen coming in with the inhale is carefully balanced with the amount of carbon dioxide expelled from the body with the exhale. If the exhale is pushed out in any way, over a period of time carbon dioxide levels are depleted and the relationship of carbon dioxide to oxygen becomes unbalanced. Eventually the body begins to compensate for this by restricting the amount of oxygen that is released from the blood into the tissues. This can feel like the breathing mechanism beginning to close down and it can be seen very clearly in people experiencing panic attacks. They are left gasping for air. The quick and traditional method of dealing with this situation is to breathe into a paper bag which allows the person having the attack to inhale their own carbon dioxide, restoring the balance in the body. Hyperventilation is more difficult to spot in chronic overbreathers.

Hyperventilation syndrome is the term used to describe chronic overbreathing. Although the debate on the existence of hyperventilation syndrome continues in medical circles, Dr Robert Fried in his book *Breathe Well, Be Well* (see Selected Reading) has shown that hyperventilation on a daily basis can lead to a wide array of disturbing symptoms such as faintness, headaches, depression, phobia, anxiety, chest pains, muscle spasms, shortness of breath and fatigue. Hyperventilation is accompanied by anxiety which may cause the hyperventilation and be exacerbated by it.

Incomplete exhalation can lead to incomplete expulsion of toxins from the body. This in turn can cause a wide variety of problems, not least of which are tension, anxiety and an inability to relax fully. Incomplete exhalation is also a feature of asthma. *Underbreathing* means that the body does not get the supply of oxygen that it needs and therefore cannot produce the optimum level of energy for daily activity. *Paradoxical breathing* is when the abdominal muscles contract on inhale. The appearance is of a person getting ready to receive a punch in the stomach. The effect is a highly inefficient method of breathing which can also be quite characteristic of the way the person approaches life in general. And finally *stammering*, a problem that blights the lives of millions of people around the world, is now treated very successfully by simply correcting the breathing mechanism.[8]

Varieties of Breathing

Because the breathing mechanism can be consciously controlled, we can choose to breathe in numerous different ways. We can breathe into any section of our lungs or into all of our lungs systematically. This is the three-phase breathing used in yoga. We can emphasise the inhale or the exhale, or breathe through our nose or mouth or both in turn. We can breathe through our right or left nostrils to balance right and left brain functioning and control cravings, or we can use breathing as a form of meditation by making sounds and movements in rhythm with the breath. The effect of each method of breathing is slightly different from every other method. Some techniques are easily learned, others can be quite difficult to sustain or complex to learn. Abdominal breathing is generally regarded as the 'correct' way to breathe. For normal daily requirements this is probably true but really there is no one right way to breathe – each method brings its own benefits. The simple process of inhale and exhale offers a range and depth of personal growth that most of us who take breathing for granted would find difficult even to imagine. The right way to breathe depends on what we want to get out of breathing. For sound physical health it makes sense to breathe fully; and to achieve optimum physical, mental and emotional performance, it makes sense to breathe consciously.

Exercises

These exercises are ones you can try at home. The first two will simply show you the power of breathing and its effect on your body. They are interesting exercises you can do with a friend and they usually have dramatic results, but please heed the caution with the second exercise. The third exercise is designed to introduce you to belly or diaphragm breathing. It can help you stay calm in stressful situations or, if done regularly, can reduce the general level of stress in your body.

1 Breathing for Balance
Find a friend to help you with this. Squat on the floor with your legs under you, facing your friend who takes up a similar position. The friend puts his or her hand either on your breast bone or on

your shoulder and gently pushes you back. The aim is not to knock you over but to test the resistance in your body, so don't push too hard. Don't put any effort into resisting, just see how balanced your body is. Then close your eyes and take six deep breaths into your belly. Feel the air going right down into your belly. Now let your friend try again. Feel the difference. Then swap over, you pushing, your friend breathing.

2 Lowering Your Centre of Gravity

CAUTION: IF YOU HAVE A WEAK BACK, CARDIO-VASCULAR DISEASE OR BRITTLE BONES DO NOT ATTEMPT THIS EXERCISE EITHER AS THE PERSON DOING THE LIFTING OR BEING LIFTED.

Again, do this exercise with a friend, preferably someone approximately your own height and weight. Stand behind your friend, place your arms firmly around his or her waist and clasp your hands in front. Bend your knees and keep your back straight. You are going to begin lifting your friend. Do so with your legs, not your back. Your goal is *not* to actually lift them, but to get an impression of their weight. They may just come up on to their toes. Now unclasp your hands. Let them take six deep breaths into their belly, eyes closed, feeling the air going deep into their abdomen. Now try to lift them again, taking the same precautions with back and legs as before. Feel the difference. Then swap over and let them try to lift you.

3 Diaphragm Breathing

Find a comfortable room where you won't be disturbed. Lie down on a bed or the floor or sit in a comfortable chair. If you need to support your neck, place a towel or small pillow beneath your neck but not your head. Loosen your belt or the waistband of your trousers or skirt. Place one hand on your chest over your heart and the other on your belly. Which hand is moving most? If your lower hand isn't moving then you are not breathing into your belly. Now gently push your belly out on the inhale. Breathe slowly in and out through your nose, allowing the belly to swell with each inhale and collapse with each exhale. Do this three or four times, then rest for a few minutes. You don't want to tire yourself out. If you like, you could take another three or four belly breaths and then relax again. You can build up the number of breaths by practising every day.

Try deep belly breathing the next time you are in an argument, heated debate or otherwise stressful situation. Mind and body are intimately connected and the physically steadying and rooting effect of breathing has a similar effect on the mind and the emotions.

Now that we have looked in some detail at the process of breathing, the place of rebirthing in the long tradition of therapeutic breathwork and tried out a few breathing exercises, let's focus more closely on rebirthing itself and what you might expect from a session.

3

☯

Expect the Unexpected

'This above all: to thine own self be true,
And it must follow, as the night the day,
Thou canst not then be false to any man.'
[William Shakespeare, *Hamlet*, Act 1, Scene 3]

According to the old cliché, you never forget your first love. Never mind first love, the first I will never forget was my first rebirthing client. A sprightly woman in her seventies with a grown-up family, Rose had never done any kind of therapy or personal-development work before. Yet, suddenly and inexplicably, she decided that she needed to do something about the way events from her childhood, over sixty years earlier, were continuing to influence her life. I was still in training at the time and having a client at all was a big boost to my confidence. I was petrified and elated all at once and, of course, I felt I was better than all the other trainees because I had a client and they didn't. It took about ten minutes for Rose to knock that little bit of egotism out of me.

I prepared for the session. It was going to go by the book, if there was a book. Rose was going to sit in my rebirthing room sipping tea. I was going to ask her amazingly insightful questions which would lead her to an equally amazing understanding of herself and her past experiences. Then she was going to resolve everything that had emerged during our conversation by breathing in the rebirthing manner for approximately one hour. That was what I expected.

What I got was very different. From the moment Rose arrived, she talked and she talked and she talked, one story after another. All her stories were interesting, but bore no apparent connection with each other and had no discernible point or direction. I was helpless. I couldn't get a word in edgeways, never mind ask a whole question. Everything I had learned or read about careful, non-directive questioning, about cognitive understanding about anything at all related to clients went out the window. How could I facilitate her understanding of her experience when I couldn't follow the direction of half of what she was saying? This was not supposed to happen. Then suddenly, in the middle of another story, she burst into tears. She had talked herself into the core of her experience and was ready to use her breathing to help her come to terms with it. She had done it all by herself. All I had done was sit there and listen.

What Happens in a Rebirthing Session?

Rose taught me my first lesson as a rebirther – to have no expectations whatsoever because invariably it is the unexpected that emerges. So what can you expect when you arrive for your first session?

You can expect the session to consist of three parts. First is usually a period of talking that lasts anywhere between fifteen minutes and an hour and a half, depending on the needs of the client. Usually in the first session a lot of this time is taken up with a case history. This is a short history of your life that tells the rebirther a little about you, your birth, childhood, your current life situation and the reasons you have decided to do rebirthing. It will also include any relevant medical information. In subsequent sessions this first part is a time for exploring the issues that have brought you to rebirthing and your experiences between sessions. The aim here is to draw the client out, to explore their past and present and to facilitate them in arriving at their own insights, understanding and plan of action to achieve the changes they desire. How it is accomplished is largely dependent on the rebirther's way of working and their interaction with the client. Some rebirthers are also trained as counsellors or psychotherapists. For most, rebirther training would contain training in counselling skills. Rebirthers also often employ techniques such a visualisation, voice dialogue, journaling, movement, affirmations, letter writing and artwork in this section of the session.

This is what you might expect, but it doesn't necessarily happen this way. If a client arrives for the session already in a heightened emotional state, they may need to lie down and begin the breathing straight away. The talking can come later. A client who is experienced in rebirthing and knows how to use the breath to resolve any issues that might arise during the session, may need very little time to talk. A small but still significant percentage of novice clients prefer to breathe with a minimum of talking. Also, some rebirthers may work mostly with the breath and sessions will then involve very little verbal exploration. This is especially true if a client is also seeing a counsellor or psychotherapist. However, for the majority of clients this period at the start of the session is quite important. Most people need to arrive at some level of understanding of what is happening in their inner lives. They find this exploration of the world inside themselves, their belief systems, emotions and their past experience therapeutic. Clients often become emotional while interacting with their rebirther in this way and issues that arise can be resolved in the next part of the session, the breathing.

This second part is the rebirth itself and it usually lasts between forty-five minutes and an hour and a quarter. There are no fixed positions for breathing but generally the rebirthee lies fully clothed on a bed or mattress covered by a blanket. Their legs are uncrossed and hands are placed by their sides. At some point in the session they may want to change position, often adopting a foetal pose, but generally there is not a lot of movement as this can be a way of distancing oneself from what is happening internally.

The breathing is the heart of the session. It is where the rebirthee really enters his or her inner world in a very experiential way. In deciding to do rebirthing, most people are seeking real and lasting change in themselves and their lives. The breathwork is where this transformation takes place but sometimes people have expectations about how that transformation will occur. Those expectations are often related to their reasons for coming to rebirthing.

Why Choose Rebirthing?

Clients choose rebirthing for many and often very varied reasons. Rose came because an important relationship from her childhood had remained unresolved for over half a century, but most of my clients have been motivated by more present-day difficulties. Some have had marital or relationship problems and decided quite rightly that their relationship would change if they could resolve some of their own personal issues. Others have been so hurt that they found it impossible to sustain any kind of intimate relationship and simply wanted to be able to trust again. A few, all women, were still living with or recovering from abuse.

Sometimes a life crisis such as a bereavement or a road accident can spur people on to take stock of their lives and highlight areas they want to change. Or they might have recently realised that conditions like shyness and lack of confidence are not something they have to labour under for the rest of their lives. Other clients have come with specific, often diagnosed disorders such as depression, anxiety and panic attacks. Because I facilitate workshops on stress management, I also get quite a lot of clients whose main aim is to rid themselves of heart palpitations, headaches, sleeplessness, or any of the numerous other symptoms of stress. Many other people have come to me for rebirthing because they are experiencing a general unhappiness, or simply because they want to get to know themselves better, find a direction in life or live that life a little more fully.

These are just some of the wide range of reasons people decide to take rebirthing sessions. Some clients arrive for their first session with only vague notions of what might transpire, but I find that quite often they have a very clear picture of what constitutes the solution to their problems. They want to learn the mechanics of how to relate, what to say or do, how to recognise the potential abuser before becoming involved with him or her. They want the symptoms, the pain, the worry to go away. They want to learn how to say no, to set boundaries, to live a little. These are reasonable expectations and they are usually explored extensively in the talking portion of the session.

But the beauty of rebirthing is that it is a body-based technique that relies on the innate wisdom of the body. As such it often bypasses the considered opinion of both client and rebirther as to what is important and what is not. What emerges in the rebirthing session proper may have no apparent connection with what rebirthee and rebirther have probed and explored earlier. A phrase I often hear from new clients after a session is 'I never thought that was bothering me'. Those who have completed a few sessions know that the breathing charts its own course and expectations are futile because they are usually transcended and greatly surpassed. The journey inwards is different for each person and in chapters 11 and 12 we will look more closely at the variety of experience made possible by this technique. But in essence everyone's journey is leading in a similar direction and, again, Rose's case serves to illustrate this well.

I knew Rose outside of rebirthing. In sessions her stories rambled, had no common theme and no apparent significance, but they were told quite eloquently using complete sentences and colourful images. In stark contrast, outside of sessions her speech was halting, limited and, at times, incomprehensible. She spoke in fragments of sentences as if articulating parts of her thoughts and leaving the rest to her listeners to work out. She appeared far less intelligent than she actually was and, as a result, the people around

her tended to dismiss her opinions and the contributions she tried
to make to conversations.

So what made the difference? What was the key ingredient in
sessions that generated such an obvious transformation in something as basic as Rose's mode of self-expression? During
rebirthing Rose got to talk uninterrupted to someone who was
really listening, not necessarily following the point, but listening
with acceptance and, in so far as it is possible to be without judgement, listening non-judgementally. The value of this non-
judgemental acceptance, or what Carl Rogers, the pioneer of
person-centred therapy, called unconditional positive regard, was
another very important lesson Rose had to teach me. People
blossom in an atmosphere of acceptance when they are simply
allowed to be who they are in the moment and I have found that
there is one common denominator in all rebirthing experiences. By
many fascinating and varied routes, people are all moving towards
the one quality that so transformed Rose's speech patterns – non-
judgemental acceptance of self.

My Self and My Ego

So what is this self? There are many, often conflicting definitions
of the word. The one I like best comes from Jack Rosenberg's
excellent book *Body, Self and Soul: Sustaining Integration* (see
Selected Reading). He defines the self as 'a non-verbal experience
of well-being, identity and continuity that is felt in the body'.[9] It
is the warm, safe centre of ourselves, the place we retreat to when
we need to replenish our inner resources. A healthy sense of self
is what enables us to take criticism without being devastated by it
and know that we can survive the loss of someone we love because
we are not that person. This sense of self begins to form early in
life, possibly while we are still in the womb[10] and needs to be
nurtured by love, approval and respect.

But this developing sense of self is not always sufficiently nurtured, or it can be damaged in some way by the kind of life experiences we will look at more fully in Part 2. When this happens, the part of the self that interacts with the world, the ego, attempts to ease the pain and restore emotional equilibrium. It does so by adopting a wide range of belief systems, behaviour patterns and other traits that are as varied as there are people in the world. These traits and patterns then become integral to our way of interacting with others.

What this means in real terms is that when a child receives disapproval for something that is a natural expression of himself, his noisy exuberance for example, he will find ways of winning back this approval. This may mean he suppresses his boisterousness, or it may lead to other behaviours like over-helpfulness, assumed charm, or deceit. All of these will win approval in other ways.

No matter what the individual adaptation, when the self is damaged by disapproval, disrespect, lack of recognition or other traumatic events, people feel pain. For me, the aim of rebirthing is to heal the damage to the self, to nurture each person's sense of self and allow it to grow by pouring on it the balm of *self*-acceptance, *self*-respect and *self*-approval. The breathing makes it possible to access the wonderful sense of peace, warmth and well-being that comes from being connected to our core. For many people this connection is possible on their very first rebirthing session although much still remains unresolved. As sessions progress and old conditioning dissolves, this experience of connection with self becomes a more regular occurrence until finally it becomes our habitual way of life.

Changing the Light Bulb

What does it take to make this happen? There is a psychotherapy version of an old joke. How many psychotherapists does it take to change a light bulb? One, but the light bulb must be willing to change. The requirements for taking rebirthing sessions are few, but one essential is that the rebirthee needs to be willing to let the technique do its work. This may seem like a statement of the glaringly obvious, but it is vitally important. Willingness is a basic ingredient and if it is missing, rebirthing will probably turn into a very pleasant dreamy period of relaxation and nothing more. This quality of willingness is sometimes quite difficult for the rebirther to recognise and especially difficult for the client to see. It is largely a question of being *ready* to change on the level of cause rather than symptom.

Most people come to rebirthing with some degree of emotional and/or physical pain or discomfort. Quite naturally they want to rid themselves of that discomfort whether it be chronic anger, depression, the debilitation of a phobia, sadness, shyness, relationship difficulties or any other issue. But the feelings we label painful are usually just the symptoms. To remove the pain, one needs to examine and resolve the underlying *causes* of that pain. And to some people this can seem more difficult than living with the pain itself.

The organisation Co-dependents Anonymous was founded for this very reason. Co-dependents Anonymous grew out of Alcoholics Anonymous (AA) when the people involved in AA realised that the spouses of alcoholics experienced great personal difficulties when the alcoholic stopped drinking. Although the non-drinking spouses had longed for the day the drinking and the pain it caused would end, sobriety, when it came, left them confused, often depressed and with a great emptiness inside. The problem was that their lives, and often their sense of purpose and self-worth, revolved around living with an alcoholic. It brought a high level of pain and suffering, but its removal meant that the non-drinker had to face themselves without the distraction of devotion to an alcoholic. For many, the only thing that changed was the daily circumstances of their lives and one pain was replaced by another. In rebirthing each rebirthee at some point faces him or herself. This can happen gently and slowly as the rebirthee grows in strength. But it does happen. For those willing and able to commit themselves, it leads very quickly to lasting resolution and peace of mind.

Sometimes people come to rebirthing wanting to ease the pain but they are unable to face the underlying causes. There is nothing wrong with this. It simply means they are not yet ready for the kind of work involved in rebirthing. For people who want to treat the symptoms rather than the causes, rebirthing is not the ideal therapy and this becomes apparent in the first or second session, if not earlier. This issue of readiness leads on to the very important topic of safety.

Safety

Safety is an important issue in any therapy but strangely I find that very few people actually ask me about it. Of the ones who do, their most frequent question is 'Will I open a can of worms?'.

There is a reason why much of the material that emerges in rebirthing is beyond the range of normal awareness. It is because we put it there. This ability to banish from our conscious mind the things we find too painful to handle is a wonderful safety mechanism built into every human being. It is not easily reversed. We do not easily tap into unconscious material before we have developed the ability to deal with it safely.

Asking whether rebirthing could open a can of worms, could bring to awareness feelings and memories so traumatic they would be overwhelming, presupposes that the rebirthee is not in control of his own rebirth. He is. Breathing is one of the body's natural and most essential functions. The breathing technique known as rebirthing is physically very gentle and relaxing and, in practising it, the rebirthee is simply allowing his own body to rejuvenate itself. The rebirther does not regress the client or guide their internal journey. That is left up to the innate wisdom of the rebirthee's body, the same wisdom that suppressed the painful material in the first place.

When people choose to do rebirthing, as with any other therapy, they are choosing to work through feelings, belief systems and past events they have, up to now, left unresolved. They have reached a state of readiness that will enable them to proceed with this task, and yes, painful material may emerge. But the suppression mechanism is still intact and the average person has a large store of diversionary tactics that protect them against moving too fast: drowsiness, coughing, talking, moving, tetany (see p. 129), scratching . . . The rebirther will normally make suggestions about how to move through these obstacles. If resistance is strong, it needs to be respected. If, for example, a rebirthee spends one session after another battling with drowsiness, perhaps the technique is not appropriate at this point in his life. But most of the time these little diversions are minor and the rebirthee chooses to move through them quickly. As they learn how to use their breath to resolve the issues that emerge into their awareness, they are able to deal with more and more difficult material. It is a growth process, a development of skills, abilities and trust in the power of their own breath. That said, there are some categories of people for whom rebirthing is not suitable.

Other Limitations

Rebirthing is not at its most effective for people on high doses of mood-altering drugs simply because the effect of the technique will be dulled by the medication. For people taking a high dose of anti-depressants who want to begin rebirthing, consult your rebirther. He or she may be able to work together with your doctor or psychiatrist. Most rebirthers do not use the technique with psychotic disorders such as schizophrenia, bi-polar disorder (manic depression), or paranoia. A strong ego structure[11] and connection with day-to-day reality is important before embarking on a journey that will transcend many of the boundaries and structures that form part of ordinary consciousness.

Ending the Rebirthing Session

When the breathing comes to its natural conclusion, it is often followed by a short period during which the client can discuss what they have just experienced and the work to be done between sessions. Or they may simply choose to rest a while until they feel ready to leave. The total process usually takes two to two-and-a-half hours.

How Many Sessions?

Clients usually ask me this question the first time we meet. There is no answer. Traditionally rebirthers recommended ten sessions and often stuck rigidly to that number. It is my experience that some clients get what they need in as little as three sessions and others require a lot more than ten. As with any therapy, when a client stays with the same therapist for a long period, the fact that they may become dependent on the therapist is always a possibility. It needs to be kept in mind and if a dependent relation-ship seems to be forming, this can become the subject of a very valuable session. Periodically reviewing the overall progress of the sessions with your rebirther can help you decide when the work is coming to a close and help you plan your next step. The same applies to the frequency of sessions. It is something to be decided between client and rebirther, although I find that two to three weeks apart suits most people.

Ways of Rebirthing

Once the technique has been mastered, rebirthing can be done in a variety of ways and settings which are geared to the needs of the rebirthee and the level of ease they have attained in working with the breath. No one form of rebirthing is better than the other. They are simply different, leading to somewhat different experiences.

Dry Rebirthing

This is the method of rebirthing I have been describing so far and the way most people begin; lying down comfortably on a bed or mattress, i.e. on dry land. It is the most gentle way of learning how to use the breath. Dry rebirthing is usually done indoors but where the climate permits it is very pleasant to have sessions out of doors. If working outdoors it is important to take precautions in relation to sunburn. Dry rebirthing can be done in one-to-one sessions or in groups. The number of rebirthers required to supervise a group rebirth depends on the size of the group. One rebirther to every four rebirthees is a good ratio. Once the rebirthee has reached a point of ease and confidence with using his breath to integrate or resolve what emerges in the session, he can move on to use rebirthing in different ways.

Mirror Rebirthing

Rebirthing while looking at yourself in a mirror can help 'drowsy' clients stay alert and aware of what is going on for them. It can also bring up very personal issues related to self-acceptance, self-image and one's relationship with oneself. Sometimes people see their face change in various ways while doing mirror breathing and the significance of this, if any, is unique to each rebirthee.

Eye-gaze Rebirthing

An eye-gaze rebirth is when two people rebirth while gazing into each other's eyes. The most obvious issue brought up by eye-gaze rebirthing is intimacy. How comfortable do we feel being this intimate with another person and with the particular person into whose eyes we are gazing? This form of rebirthing can give rise to a host of feelings about boundaries, our internal safety mechanisms, our ability to stay focused on ourselves, being seen by others and so forth. It is not generally used with novice rebirthers but is an interesting and often enjoyable experience for couples.

Water Rebirthing

In the early days all rebirthing was done in water. Most people find this a much more intense experience than dry rebirthing, so nowadays it is generally recognised that water rebirths are more suitable for experienced rebirthees who have learned to use their breath to deal with anything that might come up for them. Depending on the individual rebirthee, this level of skill with the breath may take only a few dry sessions to attain, or it may take much longer.

Water rebirthing can be done in private sessions with the rebirthee lying in his or the rebirther's bath, or it can be done in groups in a jacuzzi, hot tub or swimming pool. It can also be done in rivers, lakes, hot springs or the ocean but thorough safety precautions are vital in these settings. In group water rebirthing, rebirthees usually pair up or get into groups of three of four. They then take it in turns to support each other in the water and act as rebirthers to the person breathing. Professional rebirthers are on hand to assist when needed.

The rebirthee usually lies face down in the water using a snorkel and nose peg. Some people find putting their face in water quite traumatic. Getting into the water and submerging very slowly can help people work through this fear and what lies behind it, but if the rebirthee really doesn't want to rebirth face down they can lie on their back and be supported in this position by their partner(s).

Warm water (35–39°C) rebirthing is more likely to activate material related to birth, relationships and so forth while cold water activates fear-based issues including that of death. It is often quite difficult to get into cold water and so the rebirth usually begins before the rebirthee attempts to enter the pool. In this way the breath is used to integrate the physical reactions to the cold.

Self-rebirthing

Part of a rebirther's job is to make him or herself redundant by facilitating the rebirthee in learning how to rebirth himself. The ability to rebirth oneself requires a functional mastery of the five elements of rebirthing which we will examine in detail in chapter 11. When people reach a level of confidence in using their breath, they can begin to use the technique at home, and we will look at this in greater detail in chapter 13.

Past-life Rebirthing

I have never had what I would call a past-life memory and am an agnostic on the subject of reincarnation. However, I have rebirthed several clients who have, in their estimation, revisited past lifetimes during their rebirths. One found himself in ancient Egypt and the memory was so strong and clear it even included the sound of a river flowing and the smell of flowers and of the earth after rain. Another experienced standing alone in a Greek garden at night feeling the warmth of the evening air on her skin. Other rebirthers recount their own and their clients' more dramatic past-life memories of torture, death and murder.

What appear to be past-life memories can and do surface during rebirthing sessions and there are a small number of rebirthers who specialise in past-life rebirthing using a particular side-to-side head movement and other techniques. But, as we've seen, rebirthing is a process that is under the control of the rebirthee and his body and breath. The breath works in wonderful ways to bring forth what we need to see and are ready to work through. It has its own wisdom. Past-life memories may be encouraged but they cannot be produced on demand.

The human mind is accustomed to using symbol, archetype and allegory to arrive at understanding and resolution. Sometimes past-life experiences may be just that, memories from a previous lifetime. But sometimes they may be simply the mind's way of dealing with very difficult present-life issues. This is one reason why the rebirthee should be the one who decides that his experience was a memory from another lifetime, not the rebirther. To tell a client that their experience constituted a past-life regression is to impose the rebirther's own belief systems and interpretations on the client's perceptions. Everyone needs to arrive at their own truth. The client may eventually end up in the same place as their rebirther or they may not, but it is their journey and the 'map' the rebirther depends on for him or herself may be a very misleading one for the client.

For those who are fascinated by past-life rebirthing, you could consult Deike Begg's book *Rebirthing: Freedom from Your Past* (see Selected Reading). You may also be able to contact past-life rebirthers through national organisations. But if past-life rebirthing is all you want to do, ask yourself why. To what extent have you explored your present life and what do you hope to gain from revisiting a previous existence? A full and honest answer to these questions can be very revealing and beneficial. For those who are put off by the idea of past-life work, a belief in reincarnation is in no way a requirement for doing rebirthing.

These then are the basics of rebirthing, its form, structure and purpose. They form the broader picture of what you might expect from rebirthing. Now lets begin to focus more closely on the actual content of rebirthing sessions. In Part 2 we will explore the kinds of problems and difficulties people often experience and look at when and why these difficulties might have arisen. Some of what comes next may resonate with you and may shed light on your own feelings and life experience. You can, if you wish, use the next section of the book to begin your exploration of yourself.

PART 2

DRAWING THE MAP

Rebirthing is a journey. When people embark on a journey they like to take at least one map along with them. Maps give guidance, offer signposts when we get lost, lend the whole process a sense of security. In psychological terms a map is a theoretical sketch of the way our psyche is structured and it attempts to explain why we feel, react and generally behave as we do. There are many theories as to why human beings grow up less than totally self-confident, trusting implicitly in the bounty of the universe, capable of forming happy and lasting relationships, loving of self and others and at peace with themselves and the world. The concepts of original sin and karma and the broad sweep of philosophy form the larger canvases. The finer details have been filled in by the discipline of psychology with its vast array of explanations for why people are the way they are. These explanations are mostly focused on very early life, relationships with parents and significant adults, sibling relationships, and traumatic events in a child's life. More recently a lot of attention has been given to the phenomenon of birth itself and its far-reaching and fundamental influence on the development of the person. And more recently still, scientists have been paying attention to the life of the child before birth.

Rebirthing too has its map. It is a very minimalist map with few elaborate explanations. In the early days it consisted mostly of conclusions drawn from the birth experiences of rebirthers and their clients. Everything was related to birth and, in my opinion, some quite unrealistic and often rigid theories were developed. Over the years, the map that goes with rebirthing has been expanded and made richer by reference to older schools of psychotherapy.

This section of the book reviews my version of that map. It looks in more detail at how we are conditioned by our life experiences even when those experiences take place before we are born. These are the events and the issues that often come up in rebirthing sessions. Reading, thinking about and examining them can help you get in touch with your feelings and identify your mental patterns. The journey inward can start at any point. Reading about the issues can be a beginning or, if you are already taking rebirthing sessions, it can help you understand more fully what you are experiencing.

This particular map is the result of what I have gleaned from my experiences as a rebirthee and as a rebirther, as well as what I've learned from reading, talking to other people and reflecting on my experience. It is just one map. There are many other maps and the breathing technique known as rebirthing works equally well with all of them.

4

⚇

A Good Womb

'. . . what happens to all of us – in the nine months between conception
and birth moulds and shapes personality, drives and ambitions
in very important ways.'
[Dr Thomas Verny, *The Secret Life of the Unborn Child*]

For those who believe in reincarnation and karma, damage to the
self can be carried through from previous lifetimes. For Christians
it began with Adam and Eve. In this lifetime, however, it begins
arguably with conception itself, but certainly before birth. Until
relatively recently the medical profession paid little attention to
the mental and emotional development of the child in the womb.
In spite of the work of rebirthers, hypnotherapists and other
regression therapists, it was generally believed that the unborn
baby could not remember, interact or make choices. This thinking was, in part, based on what science knew about the development of the brain and the assumption that memories are all stored
in the brain itself. Modern technology has begun to show us
otherwise. New work by neurosurgeons and birth researchers
around the world show that capacity for memory stored in the
brain could begin as early as the first trimester of pregnancy.
What is even more significant is the discovery that the brain
produces information-carrying hormones and distributes these
hormones throughout the body. 'This adds up to one big intelligence network where the conversation is both to and from the

brain.'[12] In other words memories can be stored in the body, not just the brain.

Babies in the womb can hear. They recognise familiar voices and recoil from angry, harsh voices. They show preferences for particular kinds of music – mostly baroque composers like Mozart or Vivaldi.[13] They dislike loud, fast, dramatic music. They exercise daily, play with the umbilical cord, the placenta or each other if there are twins, and unborn babies begin to have their own dreams as early as five months.

The time spent growing in the womb is a time of total and intimate connection with the mother. She provides food, warmth, oxygen, everything the baby needs to survive. She is his world and he knows no other state than his mother's womb. This physical oneness with the mother is obvious when babies are born with foetal alcohol syndrome, thalidomide defects or drug addiction. The dangerous substances the mother takes into her body have a profound effect on the development of the baby in her womb. But the union between mother and baby is not just physical. Pregnant women testify to a psychic connection with their unborn baby – they often know what sex the baby will be before they even go to the hospital for an ultrasound scan and they feel an intense bonding with their growing child. It is an intimacy only mother and baby can share and the mother's preoccupation with the baby will later ease her into motherhood. It stands to reason then, that with such strong physical and psychic connections between them, the baby will also share in his mother's emotional and psychological states.

Scientific studies support this. From very early on, perhaps as early as the beginning of the second trimester, the foetus begins to show the signs of awareness. Foetal monitoring shows the baby's connection not only with the mother's emotional states but also with her thoughts. Unborn babies respond almost instantly to anxiety and fear in their mothers. This can be explained by the release into the mother's bloodstream of chemicals associated with these emotions. The mother's symptoms, including her increased heart rate, are mirrored by the foetus. But communication between mother and baby goes beyond the chemical connection that transmits the physical symptoms of anxiety from mother to baby. In a famous study cited by Dr Thomas Verny in his book *The Secret Life of the Unborn Child*, unborn babies demonstrated just how well tuned in they are to their mother's thoughts. Smoking produces a marked anxiety reaction in unborn babies, but a study of pregnant smokers showed that the woman didn't have to actually smoke to produce the reaction. She just had to *think* about smoking for her baby to go into a distress response.[14]

The Mother's Experience

In her excellent book *Songs from the Womb: Healing the Wounded Mother*, psychotherapist Benig Mauger explores the mother's experience of pregnancy and birth as well as that of the baby. For the mother, pregnancy is a time of heightened sensitivity, of openness to discovering unresolved personal and family issues, of vulnerability to disturbing fears – often about the well-being of her unborn child – as well as to non-ordinary states of consciousness.[15] It is impossible for a pregnant woman to avoid all stress during pregnancy and in any case bursts of anxiety do not have long-term ill effects on the foetus. What does affect the foetus is a chronic state of anxiety. Chronically anxious mothers give birth to children predisposed to anxiety and worry. Follow-up studies on the babies of anxious mothers show that as children they experience more physical and emotional difficulties than the babies of calmer mothers. The ability to learn is closely related to emotional stability and so anxiety prone babies can go on to develop learning difficulties at school which of course compounds their anxiety. Serious events such as threatened miscarriages, incomplete abortions or shocks to mother 'severely affect the foetus and are responsible for reactive behaviour well into post-natal life'.[16]

Both Mauger and Verny agree that the most common cause of prolonged anxiety in a pregnant woman is her attitude towards pregnancy, birth and motherhood. To this, Verny adds her relationship with her husband or partner.

Many factors contribute to the attitude of a woman towards pregnancy, birth and motherhood. Money worries and other insecurities can haunt a family, especially when they are expecting another mouth to feed. Does the mother really want the baby? What were the circumstances in which she conceived? Was it under pressure from a father who wanted a child or was it the other way around – she wanted a baby and he didn't? Previous miscarriages and stillbirths can cause a high level of anxiety in a woman who may be terrified of losing this baby too. Sudden bereavement can also take its toll on her peace of mind. All these affect the foetus, often quite profoundly.

What is less obvious, yet equally important, is the mother's attitude towards herself, her own body, her sexuality and giving birth. A woman who has not been able to resolve her own birth experiences, who is out of touch with her own feelings or has a less than healthy attitude towards her own body and sexuality, will not exactly be looking forward to giving birth with unequivocal joy and anticipation. She may transmit some of these attitudes to her unborn child. And it is also well documented that women who are inordinately anxious about pregnancy and birth have a more difficult time during labour and birth.

So it is very important that an expectant mother connects with her unborn child meaningfully, that she be aware of the life growing inside her in a positive and welcoming way. They need to get to know each other. The foetus is highly sensitive and will quickly pick up rejection and withdrawal from the bond growing between them. Physical and emotional problems in newborns, including depression, correlate with the quality of the relationship between mother and foetus. The unborn baby can come through some pretty bad times relatively unscathed, but he cannot handle rejection and the withdrawal of energetic contact with his mother so easily. It is known that the children of schizophrenic mothers have a high level of emotional problems due to their mother's inability to bond with them. This bonding begins in the womb.

A Man's Job

It is very important for pregnant women to have support. That support can come from her family and friends if the baby's father is no longer in the picture. But the most stabilising influence in a woman's life at this time is a loving, supportive relationship with a husband or partner (male or female) who is as interested in the baby as she is. In the past men have been dismissed or absented themselves from the process once conception had occurred. But fathers can bond with their unborn babies if they take the time to do so. They can stroke the woman's stomach, talk to the child, take an interest in his development. They can work through their own feelings around birth and fatherhood. They can learn to communicate better with their wives or partners and prepare the way for a new baby by developing a stable, happy relationship. A father is a very important figure in the life of the unborn child and an abusive or violent father can be devastating to the foetus as well as his mother.

Elizabeth's case illustrates this. Elizabeth, a twenty-eight-year-old office worker, was a child of violence. In her eighth rebirthing session she told me about her conception:

> 'My father raped my mother. That's how I came into the world. My brother too, probably. He beat her while she was pregnant with me. It was amazing. I could feel it. I know now what it was. I can tell you the effect it had. I can say it has influenced my whole life, the way I'm afraid of living, my choice of jobs, my fear of relationships. That's what I can see now but at the time it was just pure terror . . . and confusion . . . complete confusion and chaos which caused even more terror.'

51

Elizabeth was born into a relationship which continued to be violent. Her early life experiences reinforced the effect of the violence her mother experienced while she was still in the womb. But Elizabeth was adamant that the damage began in the womb, the patterns were set then and retrieving this experience through rebirthing had a profoundly healing effect on her.

Sense Memories

The experience of rebirthers is that *in-utero* and birth events are often retained as sense memories stored in the baby's body. During rebirthing sessions rebirthees often experience localised pain in various parts of their body. These kind of memories often emerge as that pain dissolves or in response to the rebirther gently touching them at the point where the rebirther senses an energetic block. When these memories are released through rebirthing the adult, with hindsight, is usually able to describe them in words and images. But the original events may have been experienced without linear time and in the form of sense impressions or a knowingness that is beyond sequence or words.

Alan's Story

Alan is a forty-year-old executive workaholic who had experienced a lifetime of struggle with life. He is a very successful man but everything, from going into a business meeting down to making a phone call to a friend, was a challenge for him. All his life he forced himself to meet the challenges, steeling himself to do even the simplest things, but in his forties with a thriving business to his name, he had run out of energy. Over several rebirthing sessions Alan traced this pattern to his mother's intense fear of life. She had a difficult and very impoverished childhood and had been abandoned by her parents at the age of ten. Alan was her oldest child and all his life she confided in him about her fears. She complained constantly about lack of money, warned him that the bank would foreclose on the mortgage. This, of course, never happened. In fact, Alan's father made an adequate living, certainly enough to cover the family's expenses, but the young Alan was not to know this. Instead he worried and spent hours thinking up ways to earn money and stave off the catastrophe his mother was sure would come some day.

Yet something was still missing from the picture. Alan felt his family history didn't fully account for his consuming fear of life. In his sixth session Alan's rebirther, having previously discussed touch with his client, felt moved to place his hands gently on Alan's chest. Immediately Alan had a womb-time experience. The feelings were of terror, chaos and a severe pain in his chest. Some time after the onset of pain Alan felt a heavy weight bearing down on him and then the whole experience simply faded away. Alan felt a lot better after the session. He was convinced it was a real memory with a very profound effect, but he had no knowledge of it outside of the session. For this reason he decided to tackle his mother and after a very slow and tactful approach he persuaded her to talk about her first pregnancy. A few days before Alan's birth, the telephone in the house had been disconnected because Alan's mother had forgotten to pay the bill. She had misplaced the money, forgotten about it and believed that they simply couldn't afford to pay. The disconnection had come at a difficult time for her and she began to despair. What was she doing bringing a child into this insecure and difficult world? What future was there for her or the baby? It would be better if he was never born. She dreaded the birth, anticipating complications, and they came in the shape of a foetal heart problem she couldn't fully explain. Alan was born by emergency Caesarean section. When he heard his mother's story, Alan understood the full depth of his own fears.

Exercises

You may, right now, have no conscious memories of your womb time and no emotional connection with it. But gathering information about what life was like while you were waiting to be born can be fun as well as enlightening. You may begin to realise that some of your fears and reactions are not yours at all but belong to your mother or father or to the collective mind of the society and era in which you were born. If you are not currently taking rebirthing sessions, the following exercises may help you uncover things you would like to explore further. If you are already doing rebirthing, they may be useful in preparing the ground for working on womb-time issues should they arise.

1 Gathering History
a If it is possible, ask your parents about your mother's pregnancy. Look for details like your mother's health, any worries about your health, any emergencies. Were there any major events in your mother's life during the pregnancy?
b Gather as much information as you can about the era in which you were born. Look at the political climate. Was there an economic boom or slump? Were you a war baby or a child of the hippie era? Are you programmed to save money, save the world or strive constantly for success? What was the social climate like? What were the trends in fashions, art and music and what do these tell you about the era? What was the prevailing attitude towards women, pregnancy, sexuality?
c Find out as much as you can about the financial situation in your family while your mother was pregnant with you. If your father was not around, what kind of support did she have?

2 Celebrating History
Contemplate the possible effects this history might have on your mental and emotional make-up. Can you trace any of your behaviour patterns, attitudes or characteristics to the events of your pregnancy? You can do this simply by thinking about it or you can turn it into a celebration of your arrival in the world by getting creative. Make a wall chart or create a painting depicting yourself

54

in the centre and surround it with images of all the influences that came to bear on you at the time. They can be positive as well as negative.

CAUTION: FOR SOME PEOPLE THIS KIND OF CREATIVE WORK BRINGS UP STRONG EMOTIONS.

5

☷

The Grand Entrance

'Because his first experience has been so rich and so
pleasant, this baby will always be an adventurer.'
[Frederick Leboyer, *Birth Without Violence*]

'A bad birth is like a thorn in the flesh which keeps getting inflamed.'
[David Chamberlain, *The Mind of Your Newborn Baby*]

Imagine you are floating weightless in a large bath of warm water.
Your body is supported perfectly with no effort from you. The
water is always the right temperature, never too hot or too cold.
There are no harsh sounds, only the gentle wooshing of your
mother's blood as it flows past and a constant, muted beat, wonder-
fully comforting, in perfect harmony with the rhythms deep within your own body. Lights are dimmed, just occasionally
brightening into a limited spectrum of colours. Sometimes there is
a gentle swaying and rocking. You have never known the desire
for food because you are nourished before you ever become aware
of needing nourishment. You have never known hunger, cold,
physical injury, the need to succeed, to earn a living, to defend
yourself, fight, strive, pay a mortgage or any of the other strains of
living in the world today. And because you have never known
them, you don't desire them. You feel totally fulfilled. And on top
of all this, from somewhere, everywhere, come the most wonderful, loving thoughts and feelings aimed directly at you. You are
living in a world of perfect contentment where every need is
catered to before you even become aware of needing.

But your body is growing and one day your bath becomes too small for you. You have to get out. Your desire triggers a reaction and suddenly the walls of your world begin to contract. The contractions come closer and closer together and you find yourself thrust head first into a narrow passageway. That too contracts in waves at once sensuously massaging your whole body and inflicting a pain you have never experienced before.

Then you're out. Depending on the era in which you were born you may find yourself between two legs planted in metal stirrups, a body lying almost flat, gravity working against you and your mother, inflicting maximum pain on you both.

Where are you? A room full of bright lights stinging your eyes. Crashing, cacophonous sounds. A sudden change in temperature. Your body is weighed down, heavy. You are being handled. Then suddenly something happens. You don't know what, but the pain in your chest is excruciating. The connection between you and your mother has been severed and you have been forced to breathe for yourself before you're ready. You're being wiped, put in something cold, held up by your legs. You have never had to straighten your spine before – agony. No loving thoughts here – just business. Maybe even some hostile thoughts – you're a nuisance, a burden, ugly. You weren't expecting them, you have no defences, they go right in. Then you are in the arms of the woman in the stirrups. You know her. She knows you. The sound is back, the thud, thud of her heartbeat. Loving thoughts, warmth. You need them. Because the shock, the pain, the hostility have gone right in and they're going to stay there.

If you have been born in the past twenty years you may have come into a room that looks more like a bedroom in the average family home. It may even be your home. The lights may not be as bright, the sounds more muted. Instead of your mother lying on her back she may have been crouching down, letting gravity work in your favour and hers. You may even be born into another pool of water almost as perfect as the one you have left. You are handled gently, respectfully and placed close to that comforting heartbeat. And without knowing it you're breathing on your own. And those feelings of love, warmth, respect, welcome, they go deep inside too and they stay there.

Whether your birth is rough, painful, dangerous or as near to perfect as is possible to get, you have moved in the space of a few hours from one world to another, from one state of existence to a radically different one. Other than death, you will never experience a change of this magnitude again in your life. And how it happens is of vital importance to how you live that life. In the words of Dr Thomas Verny:

> 'How he is born ... largely determines who he becomes and how he will view the world around him. Whether he is five, ten, forty or seventy, a part of him always looks out at the world through the eyes of the newly born child he once was.'[17]

Not so long ago people believed babies were incapable of feeling pain. Anyone who is still inclined towards this belief need only look at the photographs in Frederick Leboyer's book *Birth Without Violence*. The anguish and terror etched on to the face of a newborn baby held by the legs before a proud doctor and smiling parents is undeniable. Energetically a newborn baby is probably more open to all forms of experience than he will ever be again in his life. The kind of experience he has will affect his physical growth, his predisposition to various illnesses, his IQ, his ability to get on with others, his career preferences as well as the relationships he forms throughout his life. Hundreds of studies in universities and hospitals around the world have demonstrated the effect birth has on the physical, emotional and intellectual well-being of babies and the adults they become. They even link depression, schizophrenia and instances of violent crime to the more severe birth complications.

Dr Verny cites studies carried out in Denmark in the 1960s. Dr Sarnoff Mednick of Copenhagen's Psykologisk Institute followed the case histories of one hundred and seventy children who had been identified as vulnerable to schizophrenia because their mothers were schizophrenics. Twenty of the children went on to develop schizophrenia. Mendick wanted to know why these particular twenty children had been affected and the others hadn't. He found several common patterns relating to their mothers and their treatment in school, but his most spectacular discovery was that seventy per cent of the twenty children 'had suffered one or more complication at birth or during their mother's pregnancy'. Only fifteen per cent of the other one hundred and fifty children had complications during birth or womb time. The same doctor, in a later study of violent criminals, found that almost all of them had exceptionally difficult births.[18]

A Brief History of Birth

Babies used to be born more naturally than they are now, with the woman squatting, attended by family and midwife. In the latter half of the eighteenth century Louis XIV of France wanted to have a clear view of the birth of his children and so the mother had to lie on her back on a raised surface. The indignity to the woman and the extra pain inflicted by lying on her back were ignored. As the age of science and reason progressed, pregnancy and birth came under the almost total control of the medical profession who tended to see it as an illness rather than a natural state of being for women and the famous birthing stirrups were invented. The medicalisation of birth greatly reduced the number of deaths in childbirth, but the price was the total loss of control by both mother and child. In the 1960s, thanks to the women's movement and the farsightedness of some obstetricians and mental-health professionals, women began to take back control of birth. However, the emphasis was still not on the baby. Frederick Leboyer's pioneering work helped put the baby as much at the centre of the drama of birth as the mother. He recognised the vital importance of respecting the wishes of the newborn baby and, in so far as is medically safe to do so, the delivery team should take their cues from the baby, not from the needs and schedules of hospital and doctor. These developments in obstetrics coincided with the discovery of rebirthing by Leonard Orr and with other research into the importance of birth for human health and happiness.

As with pregnancy, a very important factor in having a relatively smooth and easy delivery is the attitude of the mother towards childbirth and motherhood. A woman who is calm and looking forward to motherhood is more likely to have a trouble-free birth than one who dreads birth and the prospect of rearing a child. In other words, a woman who has been able to work through the effects of her own birth, her attitude towards her own body, her relationship with her own mother, and who has the support of a committed partner, is going to have an easier time giving birth, and her child is going to have an easier time being born. For people who are planning to start a family, therefore, it is a good idea to research their own birth and work through the issues that arise with the help of a rebirther before the baby is conceived.

Effects of Birth

Research by rebirthers and others shows a strong relationship between types of birth experiences and particular personality traits. It is important not to get bogged down in this. Every person is unique, every life is unique, and although birth is probably the most formative influence, every person is more than their birth. Because a person is born by Caesarean, for example, it is likely that they will have a craving for physical contact. It is likely, but it is not the rule. To see people only in terms of their birth is to blinker our view of them and possibly to miss out on key information that would help us know them more fully. Labelling people according to their birth and interpreting or predicting their behaviour based on this can also be counter-productive. For many people there is comfort and shelter in a label. They begin to live up to it rather than move beyond it and moving through and beyond our experience is the focus of rebirthing.

Also there is a continuum from conception through birth, childhood and adolescence. A mother who is chronically anxious throughout her pregnancy will pass some of that anxiety on to her unborn child. This can predispose the baby to anxiety. A baby predisposed to anxiety and sensing he is not really wanted can react negatively to even the easiest of births. On the other hand, a baby who has a very peaceful pregnancy and knows he is wanted and loved, will find it easier to survive even the most distressing of births, although his mother's disposition makes it less likely that he will have a difficult birth. The cause of the mother's anxiety usually doesn't go away after the birth and the child's experience in his family will reinforce and deepen the mark a troubled birth has left on him. Traumatic experiences in childhood can also turn the predispositions so lightly formed by a relatively trouble-free birth into deeply etched personality traits.

But sometimes other factors intervene. Parents can resolve their difficulties, they can learn to communicate and grow together. They can also separate and find peace, either alone or with somebody new. They can do a lot to ameliorate the effects of birth on their child. Likewise a loving grandparent, aunt or uncle can greatly ease the effects of birth on the child so that child, at forty years old, is not just the product of his birth. He is the sum total of his womb-time experiences, his birth, his childhood and everything that has happened to him to date.

That said, it is very clear from the work of rebirthers and other breathworkers, that birth can still exert an influence so strong that it can be seen reflected in almost every facet of a person's life and personality. So let's now look at the possible effects of the more common types of birth.

Forceps

Forceps are used to pull the baby out of the birth canal if the doctor decides that for any reason the baby needs help being born. They are quite a common feature of what many people call normal births as well as births with complications, but are most associated with anaesthetised labour where the mother's ability to flow with her contractions has been compromised. A large pair of forceps is inserted into the vagina and clamped around the baby's head. The baby is then pulled out by the head. This sounds bad enough when described in words, but words don't do justice to the reality of the situation.

For a start, birthing forceps are *big*. I don't think I will ever forget the shock I felt the first time I saw a pair. I had a summer job as a nurse aid in a small hospital and was asked to be present at a delivery in case the doctor needed me to find instruments which weren't kept in the delivery room. The woman was having problems completing the delivery and, after what seemed like a very short time, the doctor called for the forceps. I couldn't believe my eyes when I saw the size of them. Watching them being inserted into the poor woman lying on her back, legs in stirrups and screaming was enough to make me cringe inwardly. I could only imagine what it was doing to the baby. Then suddenly I could feel my lunch rising from my stomach and I became aware that I was swaying back and forth in a very unbalanced way. When I looked down at my hands they were deathly white and I spent the rest of the time in the delivery room wondering what I was going to do first – faint or throw up. I wasn't surprised to find out many years later that women often associate the experience of a forceps delivery with violation, even rape.

Considering the delicate nature of a newborn baby's skull this is a potentially dangerous procedure for the baby and there is a relationship between forceps deliveries and migraine headaches later in life. Forceps leave such an indelible impression on the skull that sometimes in rebirthing the rebirther can clearly see the mark on the client's head. This also happens with cord around the neck deliveries (see pp. 70–1).

Storm's Reluctant Entrance

Storm's parents called her Storm because she was born on a stormy summer night in a small country hospital. Her mother was in labour for less than three hours but it was four o'clock in the morning and the doctor had been called out from his bed and was anxious to return to it. When Storm's mother panicked and inter-rupted the birthing process, the doctor used forceps. Storm had always been a very dependent person. Even in rebirthing sessions she would complain that she couldn't go any further and then drop into a sleep-like state that sometimes happens during rebirthing. I would then have to find ways to keep her aware and breathing fully. Once I hit on the right one – usually by getting her to talk a little – she would get over the obstruction and continue with her rebirthing session. When I pointed this out to her, Storm admitted that she wanted me to help her out and this led to a recognition of this pattern in her other relationships, particularly at work. She would begin a project then suddenly lose heart and leave it to her colleagues to complete it without her.

Some forceps deliveries resent the person who tries to help them but Storm was not one of these. She was a strong woman who was proud of the fact that she had got everything she ever wanted in life, mostly by getting other people to do things for her. It would have been easy to dislike her. But as she moved deeper into her-self she touched upon a deep store of anger at the world and particularly at the pain of being manipulated into a birth she felt she had no control over. Her helplessness was at once a form of revenge on the world and a way of controlling people.

63

Normal

A normal birth, defined as one where nothing goes wrong and medical intervention is minimal, is still a momentous event. The imaginary births described at the beginning of this chapter were both normal. Many elements of the normal birth can affect a baby very deeply. The brightness, noise, drop in temperature and rough handling of a well-meaning but medically oriented delivery team can make the world seem like a harsh and unfriendly place to be. Being rubbed clean, weighed and examined before being handed to the mother can be disorienting and frightening. Having the umbilical cord cut before it has stopped pulsating or being hung upside down and slapped can be agonising and stunning to a new-born baby who has no idea what is going on or why he's being treated in this way. Very few children have the objectivity to see that the hurtful things adults do to them may be the result of ignorance or of unresolved difficulties within the adult and have nothing to do with the child they are mistreating. Almost invariably the child blames himself. The same is true, on the most primitive of levels, for the newborn baby. The most normal of births, if not eased by the experience of a loving family, can lay the groundwork for insecurity, fear, guilt and lack of trust in life. The agony of a premature first breath, for example, can teach a child to be wary of life, that grasping at life can hurt. The pleasure and the pain of being born can intermingle, and even with normal deliveries the feeling can be that, sooner or later, pleasure turns into pain and too much pleasure feels like pain. This can be a recipe for holding back, tentativeness and a limited capacity for enjoying the good things in life.

Sondra Ray and Bob Mandel in their book *Birth and Relationships* point out that '. . . uncomplicated vaginal birth does confer important emotional advantages'. Normal-birth babies seem to accept life more easily and have a more open disposition. Things can seem to come to them more easily than to people whose birth predisposed them to seeing life as a struggle. However, normal-delivery babies can also feel unimportant and even guilty that their their birth was so easy.[19] It is possible that the foundation for this sense of guilt was laid at birth but is likely to be turned into a fully fledged personality trait by the experiences within the family. In some families birth is not talked about, but in others children are reminded over and over again about the pain they caused being born. Sometimes parents relate more easily to easy-delivery children than to more difficult births. If either of these situations apply, the resentment of siblings and the attitude of parents can easily turn a birth predisposition into guilt.

Caesarean

Caesarean sections are performed when, for a variety of reasons, the birth cannot proceed vaginally. It is often an emergency procedure designed to save the life of mother and/or baby and so is surrounded by anxiety. There may be many complications that make the Caesarean necessary and so the Caesarean procedure itself may be just one element of the whole birthing process that has an effect on the baby.

One of the most common features of Caesarean babies and adults is that they crave physical affection – hugging, stroking. This is because they missed out on the sensuality of the passage through the birth canal where their bodies are massaged by the contractions. This need for physical contact may not be apparent in all Caesareans, in fact, not being used to it and not knowing how to get it from birth, they may even shy away from contact as adults. They may or may not be the hugging kind. Or this need for affection may be focused on one person, a spouse or partner or someone with whom they feel comfortable being affectionate.

Caesareans have been rescued from a potentially dangerous situation. They have not been able to do it normally or do it their way. The Caesarean baby misses out on the struggle down the birth canal and therefore he also misses out on the sense of achievement that may accompany that success. This is especially true of babies born before labour has begun.[20] As with all birth effects it is difficult to say that this predetermines specific kinds of behaviour, but working from the other end of the spectrum it is possible to trace adult behaviour back to specific birth experiences. Lack of struggle and the artificial removal of the baby from his mother's body means there has been no natural separation. When this is combined with the delay in bonding due to the fact that both mother and baby are affected by anaesthetic, the Caesarean baby may have trouble separating from his mother when the time comes to do so (see chapter 6). Later in life he may have difficulty maintaining a sense of self and his boundaries in relationships.

Deike Begg points out that planned Caesarean babies (no labour) can become timid adults lacking in confidence.[21] Babies trigger the onset of labour so the planned Caesarean baby has been removed suddenly from the security of the womb before his time. He also arrives in a world where his anaesthetised mother is not able to respond to him immediately. He may feel totally abandoned and, as an adult, he may that feel he can't take the initiative or do things himself without the permission of others. Caesareans often give out the message that they want things done for them, and then resent the helper or criticise them because they are not doing the job correctly. Studies are also beginning to show links between the use of drugs during birth and drug addiction in later life.[22]

Cathy – A Classic Caesarean

Cathy was one of my earliest clients and one of the first to revisit her birth in sessions with me. She was born by Caesarean after a very long labour which almost ended in death. She sees the Caesarean as the least influential aspect of her very difficult birth, yet she has had a life-long aversion to being part of a group, any group. For her, group membership means having to think and behave according to group rules and values and she has never been able to be part of a group and be true to herself at the same time.

There are advantages to belonging to a group – contacts, job opportunities, the development of social skills – and, in her opinion, she has missed out on all of them. At the same time she has always craved the security of belonging and being like everyone else.

Cathy is also physically clumsy and awkward because, like many Caesareans, she has a limited concept of her own body, its size and the way it moves. Involvement in sports as a child could have helped her overcome this but Cathy was too embarrassed and shy to take part. Again, birth is part of a continuum of experience. Cathy's mother had a poor body image herself, very low self-esteem and conflicting feelings about her own sexuality. All this contributed to her having a difficult delivery. These attitudes didn't disappear after the birth. Throughout her childhood, Cathy's mother told her she was fat and unattractive. This constant barrage of negativity stopped Cathy from engaging in the activities that could have helped her overcome one aspect of her birth, physical awkwardness. Instead a predisposition turned into a very noticeable personal characteristic.

Induced

Babies initiate labour. In induced births, labour is triggered not by the baby in his own time but by a synthetic form of oxytocin, the hormone that causes contractions. Induction is performed for a variety of reasons, sometimes for very sound medical considerations, and sometimes for the convenience of the doctor or the parents. Either way, the baby is being born before his time. Induced deliveries can be long and very painful. The mother is labouring in response to a chemical flowing through a drip, not in harmony with her body's instincts and rhythms and not in harmony with her baby. The mutual regulation, the give and take between mother and baby so vital to a healthy relationship as well as to the child's self-esteem, is not present. The effects of these elements alone can be far-reaching.

Lack of harmony with the mother in giving birth may lead to lack of that give and take in adult relationships where two people show flexibility in taking the initiative, getting things done and adapting to each other's ways and needs. Induced births can find the dance of a relationship difficult and, as Ray and Mandel have pointed out, may insist that their partner makes decisions, takes the initiative, talks them into things.[23] Induced birth means being born at the behest of someone else. They never really made the choice. Being talked into something, even as simple as where to go for dinner, is not making a choice. And when we go along with what someone else chooses, we can feel angry and resentful even if the outcome is to our liking. This anger can be turned outwards, making for difficult relationships, or inward, leading to depression or other difficulties.

Dr Verny has also related induction to both sexual sadism and masochism.[24] The journey through the birth canal is a mixture of pleasure, sometimes of a sexual nature, and pain. In induced births the balance is heavily in favour of pain. Combine this with the anger pain causes, low self-esteem and other factors within post-birth and childhood experiences and one possible outcome is this often dangerous form of sexual inclination.

Premature

Babies can be premature for a wide variety of reasons both physical and emotional, and these need to be taken into account when looking at the effects of premature birth. The mother's fears, including that of losing the baby, can be factors in bringing about a premature delivery and these will leave deep marks on the new-born. Prematurity, particularly of a few weeks or more, creates medical emergencies. Or the delivery may be by Caesarean as a result of a life-threatening situation. Either way, the anxiety this causes for the parents and medical team leaves its own imprints. But one of the most common characteristics of premature babies relates directly to being put in an incubator immediately after birth.

Incubator babies can grow up feeling cut off from full engagement in life and relationships and they often describe this feeling as a glass wall between them and life. Even people who know nothing about their birth or the influence birth can have, talk about this glass wall, never associating it with an incubator.

Again the effect of this depends on many contributing factors. If the contact between mother and baby is very restricted immediately after birth, bonding will be delayed or severely limited (see chapter 6). A happy, stable mother supported by a loving father/partner can do a lot to make up for this initial separation, but often interrupted bonding can lead to a less than easy and spontaneous relationship between parent and child. This can compound the sense of isolation and abandonment premature babies tend to feel. It can also develop those tendencies into full-blown character traits. Because they have great difficulty breaking through that energetic glass wall, premature babies can grow up to become loners. The craved intimacy, when it comes, can often feel claustrophobic and in some cases this desire for intimacy, combined with an inability to sustain it, leads to sexual promiscuity. But change the family and the same kind of birth can have an apparently opposite effect. Prematures who are severely criticised, put down or compared unfavourably to others can become very insecure children and adults and cling to relationships, even abusive ones, to avoid that desperate feeling of isolation.

Owen – the Reluctant Romeo

Owen came to rebirthing when he was twenty-seven. He was a very clear-sighted young man who recognised that he needed help when his first real relationship began to flounder. Owen had spent his teens and early twenties having a series of intense, agonising crushes on various women but never forming a relationship with anyone. Then he met Rhonda. His dream had come true. She was funny, attractive and shared many of his attitudes and interests. Yet three dates into the relationship he began to feel panicky around

69

her, almost as if he couldn't breathe. Then he began to feel panic at the thought of meeting her and eventually this turned to anger and repulsion which he directed at her. He wanted to get out of the relationship that was suffocating him. They had a blazing row in which he accused her of being possessive and domineering and she screamed at him that he was cold and aloof. He was stunned that he had destroyed the dream he had had for over ten years.

Owen spent a long time working through childhood issues that included being bullied in school. Then in one session he remembered his mother telling him that he had almost killed her. As far as he could recall she had only said it once, when he was very young. It triggered a rage that consumed his whole body. He was having a birth memory. His birth was long and extremely painful and he could distinctly feel his mother's anger and resentment and the rage he felt at her for rejecting him in that way. Then the pressure and the pain were over and there was chaos, panic, he was being rushed somewhere roughly, his chest rubbed. Then he was alone for a long, long time. He remembered longing for someone to come to him and believing nobody would so he had better get on with being alone.

Owen was two months premature. The labour was very long with insufficient lubrication in the birth canal – agonising for both mother and baby. Owen was put in an incubator in a special-care unit of the hospital where his parents could only look at him through a window. The loneliness he experienced in the incubator was excruciating but he had learned to live with it and accept it as his fate. He saw his birth clearly as a blueprint for his life – desperate longing for connection with somebody; the connection, when it came, feeling like suffocation and death. The whole situation was suffused with an intense and very confusing anger, his own and his mother's, his and Rhonda's.

Cord around the Neck

A similar push-pull dynamic can be seen in the relationships of many babies born with the umbilical cord wound around their neck. Babies can become entangled in the cord at birth and some-times this can tighten around their neck cutting off their supply of oxygen and causing their skin to turn blue. It is a potentially life-threatening situation. In these cases birth and death are very closely enmeshed, living fully can become very uncomfortable, intimacy can spark off primal fear. These patterns can manifest in any area of life including career, relationships, any projects undertaken. Cord around the neck babies can desire fulfilment, involvement, commitment and can enter into relationships and jobs with enthusiasm only to push away success just as it is within their grasp. Cord difficulties which bring the baby to the point of death along with conditions such as eclampsia (severe high blood pressure in the mother) and placenta previa (placenta blocking the exit from the womb) are classified by Dr Verny as severe birth emergencies. These were the kind of severe birth complications Dr Mendick associated with schizophrenia and violent crime (see p. 59). On a less serious level, cord around the neck babies can have a higher than average number of throat problems and they often dislike the feel of clothing around their neck.

Breech

A breech birth is when the baby, normally born head first, presents himself at birth either feet or bottom first. Sometimes the doctor or midwife may try to turn the baby in the womb and this can be very painful. Ray and Mandel have pointed out the importance of looking at why a baby, who instinctively knows how to be born, would present the opposite way around. It may be linked to his sensing the attitude of his parents or their anxieties about having a baby and obviously this would have a psychological effect on the baby over and above the breech presentation. He may not want to be born.[25] This can establish a similar dynamic to the cord around the neck babies who desire intimacy yet repel it when it gets too much for them. However, one of the main features of a

71

breech birth is the pain it causes the mother. Depending on the mother's subsequent reaction to the baby and the family dynamic the baby is born into, this can lay the foundation for guilt and a fear of hurting people, particularly women. Deike Begg has found that breech babies may have trouble finding their direction in life, often not hitting upon the right path until their thirties or forties.[26] There is also a slight correlation between breech births and learning difficulties in children.[27]

A Message to Mothers

Women often feel guilty about the birth of their children, particularly if that birth is traumatic, painful or highly medicalised. They may want to repair the psychological damage they think the birth may have had on their child and this affects the way they relate to their children. If you feel this way, remember that you weren't the only person involved in the birth. Your baby also played his or her part. The baby initiates labour and while the causes of breech presentation or cord around the neck are not clear, this kind of birth is not something the mother should blame herself for. If you've had a difficult time giving birth, you may need to focus on yourself for a while, giving yourself the attention you need, rather than feeling sorry for or over-protecting your child out of guilt.

We've looked at a few of the most common birth types. They are categorised by their principal feature but any one birth can combine several of the features listed above, all of which have an influence on the baby. The more severe the complication, the deeper the effect, near-death experiences being the most traumatic. Knowing your birth experience can help you understand some of your most common behaviour patterns, the dynamics of your relationships with other people, and may even illuminate the motivations behind your choice of partner. The more details of your birth you know about the better because each feature of the experience may have influenced a different aspect of your behaviour.

Exercises

1 Discovering Your Birth

If it's possible, ask your mother or father about your birth.

2 Getting in Touch with Feelings

Read Frederick Leboyer's book *Birth Without Violence* (see Selected Reading) and note the feelings it generates in you.

3 Celebrate Your Birth

Once you have established the main features of your birth, meditate on the way this experience has played out in your life. Use categories like: work, intimate relationships, friendships, how I feel about myself and my body, money and success, children, etc. Just as with the exercise on celebrating your womb time (see p. 54), you can get creative and celebrate the day you came into the world. If you are not very happy about being here and don't see your birth as a cause for celebration, maybe it's time to work through the issues that are disturbing you.

6

☙

Making the Bond and Breaking It

'If the early bonding relationship breaks down
completely, the type of disturbance to the Self can be
so severe that treatment is difficult or futile.'
[J L Rosenberg, *Body, Self and Soul*]

After the momentous experience of birth, the baby comes into the
world without the boundaries, without the fully formed ego that will
protect him in his new life outside his mother's body. He's not yet
able to make the distinction between himself and his environment.
You can see this by holding something interesting, a bright toy or
rattler, in front of a baby. He will respond with interest but when the
toy is removed he won't try to find it. If he can't see it, for him it
doesn't exist. He is the world, the world is him. There is little sense
of separateness. And, on top of this, he is totally helpless. He can't
feed himself, he has no control of his bowels, he can't even move
from where his mother or father has placed him. His only power lies
in crying and screaming but if the adults in his life don't respond to
his crying, he is totally powerless. This baby, who is still at one with
the world yet physically totally powerless, is super sensitive to all
the experiences that come his way. For this reason the early minutes,
weeks and months are vital in developing a solid sense of self. And
the first step in developing this sense of self is to learn to trust that
he will be able to get what he wants and that his world supports him.[28]

Forming the Bond

The first person a baby learns this trust from is his mother. The very deep, intimate bond between mother and baby that began in the womb needs to be developed further in the first six months or so after birth. The baby needs a lot of eye contact with his mother so he can see himself reflected in her gaze lovingly and with total approval. He needs to be fed when he is hungry, kept clean and warm. He needs to be held and cuddled and adored. He learns to adapt to her and the family in which he lives, but she and the family also adapt to him. This process teaches him that he can trust and that he can make things happen. It teaches him who he is and that it is okay to be that person. And if all goes reasonably well the baby will begin to trust himself as well as the world.

But life rarely runs with text-book perfection. Things go wrong. Sometimes mother and baby are separated shortly after birth, often due to illness, and vital bonding time is missed. For older generations this may have been common practice in hospitals. Dr Thomas Verny points out that 'As little as an hour spent together after birth can have a lasting effect on both mother and child . . . babies [of bonding mothers] almost always are physically healthier, emotionally more stable and intellectually more acute than infants taken from their mothers right after birth.'[29] Bonding women find the tasks of motherhood easier and fathers who are involved in the process at every stage, including birth, bond just as well with their babies as mothers do. But all the same factors that influence a mother's attitude to pregnancy and birth affect her ability to bond with her baby. As long as they remain unresolved she may be physically present for the baby but energetically not there at all, and with his fine-tuned sensitivity the baby will sense this. So too will children. And a child who is not really seen by his parents is affected on every level.[30]

In the psychoanalytical view of things, the first few months of life are devoted to taking things in, mainly orally. The baby takes in love through his skin when touched, through his eyes when looked at and through his mouth when fed. This is the time for breastfeeding and sooner or later the baby is going to start biting the breast. The mother may want to change to bottle feeding at this time but how she handles the changeover is very important. The child bites because that's what he does, not to hurt her. If her anger at the pain is directed strongly at him, the breast is suddenly and angrily withdrawn, and the child is blamed, then he has his budding sense of trust and esteem damaged. It has been the practice in the past to feed babies to a schedule, not in accordance with the baby's needs. A baby left hungry or force fed, a baby who can't make sufficient eye contact with his mother or who is forced to prolong eye contact in order to allay some fear inside her, a baby who is insufficiently cuddled and caressed, has his sense of powerlessness reinforced. He misses opportunities to develop his sense of self so vital to his future mental and emotional health.

He can take this into adulthood. A baby who doesn't develop basic trust in life can become a depressed, distrusting adult who has difficulty forming and maintaining relationships. A baby with an inadequate sense of self can become an adult who constantly seeks closeness with others to the point where he becomes smothering. He may also be willing to accept the most horrific abuse rather than separate from his partner.

Breaking the Bond

Babies grow and their natural impulse to maturity dictates that this bonding phase will end and the child will develop a sense of self as separated from his mother. If his self has been nurtured and his needs taken care of, this building of boundaries between himself and his mother will be a natural and untraumatic event. As the child begins to move and crawl he can now, to an extent, control where he wants to be and he can grasp and grab the things that catch his attention. He begins to realise that mother is mother and that mother is a separate person. In fact the world is filled with people who aren't him. This happens on a physical, psychic and energetic level and the baby who learned to trust the world can now explore it and test it. All the time his boundaries, that flexible energetic demarcation line that protects the self, are growing stronger.

But what if things don't go according to the guidelines? What if the mother is emotionally needy, if she didn't get the nurturing she needed as a child and is not getting it now from the baby's father? She may see the baby as the fulfilment of her own needs, the loving companion she has always craved. For any or all of these reasons she may have great difficulty letting go of the bonding phase. She may resent and feel threatened by the infant's growing independence and try to prolong the closeness by disapproving of the signs of independence. At this stage and into toddlerhood children begin to test their world and everything in it, including their parents. It is their natural drive to learn. But a parent who is still clinging to their child and does not quite see them as a separate individual can interpret this as deliberate boldness, something the child is doing to them personally. If this happens the baby may not be able to fully separate from his mother. And if he can't separate from his mother, he may not be able to develop adequate boundaries between himself and others.

Unhealthy Dependence

A person with weak boundaries feels other people's feelings. When their partner, family or close friend is in a good mood, they feel good. When their partner is depressed, they feel down and they believe that this congruence of feeling is love. It is their job to make the people around them feel better and they suffer almost physical pain when other people disapprove of them. They are wide open to manipulation and are easily convinced that they are to blame for things that have nothing to do with them. For this reason, a person without boundaries is devastated by criticism and works very hard to be liked. Relationships are a roller coaster of emotional highs and lows and often, as the years go by, the highs become fewer and the lows so prolonged that they are numbed by depression or addiction. People with inadequate boundaries gradually lose contact with their inner self and, as rebirthing clients, they are often the ones who complain that they don't know who they are or what they want. Of course, given a different set of circumstances, a different disposition, the child could go in the opposite direction and protect himself by developing rigid boundaries. A person with rigid boundaries keeps everyone at arm's length because they are afraid to let others get too close. In relationships they may be withdrawn, avoid intimacy and use rudeness and verbal cruelty to keep people at bay.

Mona's Story

Mona is an example of someone who had never broken the connection with her mother. She came to me for rebirthing sessions after ten years of marriage to a man who was generally a good husband but who suffered bouts of depression. Her husband never hit her but he seemed to blame her for anything that went wrong in his life, even if it was only poor service in a restaurant. Mona was anxious, exhausted and very reserved. She gave the impression of someone always on the lookout for people's reactions before she would let any of herself be seen.

As she talked and moved through sessions it became clear that Mona was bound to her husband in a very unhealthy way. She took responsibility for making every wrong right and even took the blame for things that had nothing to do with her. She found it hard to understand that when he came home in a bad mood she didn't have to spend the whole evening cheering him up, that she didn't have to feel his feelings.[31] But in the middle of her fifth session she had a memory from the first few months of her life. She was being held on her mother's shoulder and the experience was so clear she could even see the pores of her mother's skin. And she knew then, even though she was so small she couldn't yet support her own head, that she existed to fulfil her mother's needs for love, support and nurturing . . . things her mother had not experienced in her own childhood. Mona knew then that her job was to be whatever her mother needed her to be. The memory was quickly forgotten, but Mona spent her first forty years trying to work out what other people wanted her to be and struggling to be whatever that was. In that rebirthing session the bond between Mona and her mother was broken. She had a lot more work to do developing boundaries and negotiating the changes she needed in her marriage, but reliving the original memory was what empowered her to do it.

Exercises

A boundary can be a difficult concept to grasp. Sometimes it is easier to begin with getting to know your physical boundaries. The first exercise can help you establish these boundaries around your body, but you need the help of a friend with whom you feel comfortable. The second and third exercises can be done alone. You will need a quiet room where you feel at home and won't be disturbed. You'll also need a paper and pen.

1 Know Your Boundaries
This exercise is done with a friend. Stand facing each other on opposite sides of the room. Take a few deep breaths to bring your awareness fully inside your body. Now begin to walk towards each other very slowly. Be aware of everything you are feeling. When you begin to feel uncomfortable with the closeness of the other person tell them to stop coming towards you. This is your physical boundary with this particular person. Did you tell them to stop coming towards you at the point when you became uncomfortable or did you let them come closer than you would really have liked? If so, why? Did you stop them before you became uncomfortable? If so, why? Does this mirror patterns in your life?

79

2 Setting Boundaries

Pick a situation in your life where you feel you need to set limits. It could be something simple like finding time to rest during the day, or something more complex like cutting down on the time you spend caring for a family member. Spend some time thinking about the circumstances and then make a list of all the things you are prepared to do and the things you no longer want to do in relation to this situation. You may have to get someone else to take over some tasks for you. Who? How are you going to approach them? How do you feel when you think about setting limits for yourself? Consult the section on affirmations (see chapter 13) to help you with this.

3 Boundaries Checklist

Tick the box that applies to you. Then look at the results and decide for yourself if your boundaries need a little work. Consult a rebirther for help with this.

CHARACTERISTIC	[RARELY]	[SOMETIMES]	[OFTEN]
1 You ignore your own feelings.	☐	☐	☐
2 You feel other people's feelings quite strongly.	☐	☐	☐
3 You feel responsible when someone else is in a bad mood.	☐	☐	☐
4 You try to make people feel better.	☐	☐	☐
5 You try to make situations better for people.	☐	☐	☐
6 People take you for granted.	☐	☐	☐
7 You do what others want even when it's not good for you.	☐	☐	☐
8 You give a lot in relationships and get little in return.	☐	☐	☐
9 You have difficulty letting people get close to you.	☐	☐	☐
10 You freeze up when talking to particular people.	☐	☐	☐
11 You pretend to agree with people even when you don't.	☐	☐	☐
12 You feel people don't see the real you.	☐	☐	☐
13 You give other people's views priority over yours.	☐	☐	☐
14 You hide your opinion from others.	☐	☐	☐
15 You are frightened by anger.	☐	☐	☐
16 You are disturbed when people disagree with you.	☐	☐	☐

(cont)

CHARACTERISTIC	[RARELY]	[SOMETIMES]	[OFTEN]
17 You are embarrassed by someone else's behaviour.	☐	☐	☐
18 Criticism really hurts.	☐	☐	☐
19 You stay in abusive relationships.	☐	☐	☐
20 You have difficulty saying NO.	☐	☐	☐
21 You give too much time to others.	☐	☐	☐

7

❦

The Guiding Light

' "Before I got married I had six theories about bringing up children;
now I have six children and no theories." . . . nothing renders us
less "all-knowing" than having the responsibility
of raising children on a daily basis.'
[John Wilmot, Earl of Rochester and Wayne Dyer,
What Do You Really Want for Your Children?]

Parenting is probably the most difficult job in the world. No books
on parenting, no courses or workshops can fully prepare people for
the day-to-day reality of being a mother or father. Parenting
requires enormous amounts of love, commitment, patience, time
and energy. For parents who freely, clearly and consciously choose
to have a baby this can be a major undertaking involving
substantial changes in lifestyle and outlook. For parents who don't
make a clear choice or who don't really want the baby and continue
to feel this way after birth, parenting can become a very heavy
burden. Truly wanting a child gives both parents and children a
head start.

But no parent is perfect. No parent can control the impact of
every experience on their child, nor should they. To do so
would deprive the child of the opportunity to grow, make
mistakes and deal with the world in his own way. A child's life
is influenced by many powerful forces – school, their peers, the
media, society in general – but that said, parents are their
primary educators. They mould their children in fundamental
ways, teaching them the skills they will need to navigate their

journey through the world. Children born to parents who are themselves damaged and who are not aware of the behaviour that damage can give rise to, will be moulded by their parents' neuroses as much as by their love. So let's look at some aspects of parenting.

The Way I See It

Most of us grew up in households where there was a constant refrain, a phrase or idea repeated over and over again. I remember being swaddled in hated interlock vests with impossible rubber buttons to the tune of 'N'ere cast a clout till May is out'. But many of the refrains were far more difficult to recognise and more damaging.

Parents who have not been able to resolve their own major fears, obsessions or prejudices can pass these on to children who are too young to know that the picture of the world that is being painted for them is not necessarily reality. It is just their parents' view of things. If a parent talks about their fears constantly to their children or bases their parenting practices on those fears, he or she can pass a distorted view of the world on to the next generation. The parent's view then becomes the child's view and the child will go out and live his life from this perspective. If a child picks up an attitude of trust and openness towards life he will embrace opportunities secure in the knowledge that the world is his oyster. On the other hand, if parents see the world as hostile, dangerous or the proverbial 'vale of tears', the child is pre-programmed to anticipate struggle and opposition at every step. Parents may influence their children without realising it or they may do so deliberately out of the best possible intentions – to prepare their child for the difficulties they see lurking in the future. Some issues that are subject to distortion and the effects on children are as follows.

Parental Issue and Possible Effects on Children

Money
Insecurity, feeling responsible for supplementing family income, workaholism, choosing career/mate primarily for money, fear of money running out, obsession with financial security, paralysis around money, anger/contempt for wealthy people.

Dirt/Germs
Severely restricted play, suppression of spontaneity, obsession with cleanliness, repressed anger.

Danger
The world is a dangerous place, restricted play, fear of taking risks, suppressed aliveness.

Haves and Have Nots
Wealth is tainted, inability to make or hold on to money, destined to be the underdog, can't get what he wants, no point in trying, apathy, anger, feeling a victim and powerless to do anything about it, fear or obsession with failure/success.

Sex
Disgust, sexual hang-ups, sexual dysfunction, promiscuity.

Sexuality
Trapped in sex role stereotyping, distrust of either sex, prejudice, feelings of inferiority/superiority as a man or woman, difficulty forming nurturing relationships, game playing, limited intimacy, forced/endured sex.

General Prejudice
Homophobia, racism, anti-Semitism, fear of difference, rigidity within self.

Exercises

For these exercises you will need a comfortable, private space, a pen and paper and your imagination. The first exercise is intended to help you identify your own fears and obsessions and where they came from. The second exercise allows you to use your imagination to create a world where these fears don't exist. You can tap into this world any time by going inside your imagination.

1 Your Fears, My Fears
List your parents' fears, prejudices, obsessions. How many of them are now yours and how many originated with your parents or other important people in your young life?

2 A Perfect World
Choose one item from the list you made in the previous exercise. Begin with something that doesn't have a huge effect on you. You can go on to something more difficult later. Now imagine a world where this fear/belief/obsession no longer exists. Get into it, feel it, let it expand. How do you feel? If that worked for you, you might like to move on to something else from your list which has a stronger emotional charge for you, but don't go beyond what is comfortable.

Consult the section on affirmations in this book (see chapter 13) to help you rid yourself of your attachment to this view of the world or get a copy of the book *You Can Heal Your Life* by Louise Hay (see Selected Reading).

The Supreme Court

From the day he is born, a baby is taught what is and is not acceptable. His smiles and gurgles are rewarded with high-pitched praise and tickles. But when a baby refuses to smile, the adults in his life want to know what's wrong with him today and try to coax a smile out of him with funny faces, toys and tickles. This is all quite innocent and teaches the baby very valuable lessons about how to relate to others. But as the child grows older, the playful coaxing can turn into angry criticism. The criticism is only partly fuelled by concern – if a child is quiet and introverted, does that mean he's depressed? Unfortunately it's also prompted by the belief that smiling, amenable and outgoing (or any number of other traits) is the way to be. It's the way everyone *should* be. And when things aren't the way they should be some people become uncomfortable, don't deal with their own discomfort and try to change the person who is causing that discomfort.

Almost every aspect of life is judged and ranked according to a hierarchy of values which go unquestioned by most people. Tall and thin is good, short and fat is not; nice is good, rude is not; ambitious is good, indifference to getting ahead is not. In some circles ruthlessness is good, its opposite is not; winning is good, losing is not. The list is endless and so are the methods used to push children into living up to standards. They vary from encouragement and praise to bullying, comparing them with other children, public humiliation and a refusal to recognise their achievements. Children can encounter this pressure to conform not just in the home but in school, among their peers, anywhere in fact.

What does this teach children? For those who don't measure up to what is acceptable, it teaches them inadequacy, shame and doubt. How they handle this damage to their self-esteem varies. They can become depressed or rebellious, they can give up, or they can work very hard to fit into the mould that has been presented to them. Relationships and careers can be based on measuring up and lots of people manage to convince themselves and others that they really are who they appear to be. Then something happens, the children leave home or middle age prompts them to take stock. Suddenly they don't know who they are and they don't know the person they have been married to for thirty years. When this happens people can either sink into despair or they can work through the layers of conditioning to find their core selves and begin to set free the aspects of themselves they have forgotten existed. I have had many rebirthing clients, men and women in their sixties and even seventies who were beginning to take stock of themselves and their lives after bereavement or retirement.

For those who do measure up, naturally life is easier. But few people measure up in every area and few people are outgoing, cheerful, confident and achieving every minute of the day. For them, measuring up can also become a prison where the strong and reliable must always be strong and reliable, the clown must always be the clown, the achiever must always achieve . . . For those who measure up, as well as for those who don't, part of the self must be kept hidden, rejected, suppressed. And if it is kept hidden long enough it drops out of sight only to surface as illness, depression, discontent or a host of other phenomena.

Exercises

What was acceptable in your family and what was frowned upon? You can use the following exercises to examine your family values as well as your own. You'll need a pen and paper.

1 Can Do, No Can Do

What was acceptable in your family and what was not? Make a list using categories like jobs, body shapes, personality traits, activities, holidays, possessions, etc.

2 The Classic

Pick two or three items from your list. Put the first one at the top of a sheet of paper and without thinking too much about it write down every word that comes to mind that you associate with it. This can help you to understand the judgements and value systems you operate within. Do the same with the other items.

3 My Body Beautiful

Look at yourself in a full-length mirror. Start with your head and work downwards. Examine every feature slowly – your face, your hair, your height and size, your clothes. How many features do you make a judgement about? Can you, for example, note that you have brown hair and leave it at that? Or do you say 'Brown hair – dull, boring, not as nice as X's hair', or 'Brown hair – fabulous, lovely highlights, better than X's hair'. Judging positively is better than judging negatively but not judging at all is the ideal.

Were you able to do this exercise? If not, ask yourself very gently why? Are there issues you need help dealing with?

Only Happy Campers Allowed

Tanya cried the day her boss wrongfully accused her of stealing. Crying in front of her boss was the last thing she wanted to do, the last thing she felt like doing, but it happened. 'I was furious with her. There I was being accused of something I didn't do by a woman who had been out to get me for a long time. I wanted to scream at her that I have crossed wires, that I cry when I'm angry so ignore the crying. But I couldn't. It would just have made me look more pathetic.' What do you do when you get angry? Do you shout, scream, throw things, hit people? Do you smile, become extra nice and hate yourself for being so untrue to yourself? Do you eat? Do you hold your breath and walk away or do you cry like Tanya did?

Tanya was a participant in a personal-development course I ran that included a rebirth on every second session. It took several sessions for Tanya to realise that she cried when she was angry not because she had some sort of mental wires crossed, or because she was a 'typical woman' like her husband suggested, but because she was terrified of showing her anger. Most of the time Tanya could bite back anger and deal with the situation in what she thought was a responsible and reasonable way. But when the anger was so strong it threatened to burst forth and cause damage, Tanya sublimated it into something non-threatening. She cried. And every time she went through this routine she was re-enacting something that had happened a thousand times with her mother.

Like many people, Tanya's mother couldn't handle anger. Perhaps this was because her own mother was a very angry person. When Tanya expressed anger, sorrow, pain, frustration or any of the emotions we label negative, her mother became almost hysterical. She cried loudly and demanded to know why Tanya was hurting her so much. The message Tanya got was that her anger was so hurtful to others that she should never express it –

even when her career was being destroyed over something she didn't do.

Emotions are a child's currency. They are a large part of how he expresses his needs and desires, of how he express his core self spontaneously and unselfconsciously. But in many households certain emotions are taboo because they're 'not nice' or because the adults in the house can't handle them. Sometimes a child's spontaneous joy and high spirits bring anger and even violence from parents. Sometimes, like Tanya, it is sorrow or anger that draws disapproval. Children need to learn responsible and appropriate ways of expressing emotions but when a child's emotions are disallowed, he learns that a part of himself is bad or wrong and has to be suppressed. Then the river of emotion goes underground, becomes invisible and surfaces in a different guise somewhere else. Sometimes this sublimation is both healthy and socially acceptable. Anger, for example, can be channelled into sport. But often it is destructive. Suppressed emotions can turn into depression, diseases, neuroses and self-destructive behaviour like Tanya's.

Exercise

1 Bad Feelings, Good Feelings
Fill out the following chart to examine what kinds of emotions you were allowed and not allowed to express in your family. Were there some emotions you simply did not express? You may want to add more emotions to the left-hand column.

EMOTION	MOTHER'S REACTION	FATHER'S REACTION	HOW IT HAS AFFECTED YOU
Anger			
Sorrow			
Helplessness			
Joy			
Confidence			
Emotional strength			
Sexual attraction to boys/girls			
Frustration			
Disappointment			
Exuberance			

How have these prohibitions affected your life? How have they restricted you or locked you into one kind of behaviour? And if your parents were very comfortable with a wide range of emotions, how has this affected the way you live and express yourself?

Inappropriate Needs

In an ideal world the ideal parent is someone who has reached a high level of maturity and emotional self-sufficiency. If they feel they need support, love, closeness, comradeship, sex, friendship, reassurance, praise, protection or to be taken care of, they turn to an intimate relationship with a spouse or partner. If there is no spouse or partner, those needs can be fulfilled by friends, family, or the many support organisations within society. An ideal parent takes care of their child, not the other way around, and the one person a parent ought not expect to fulfil their adult needs is their son or daughter.

But nobody is an ideal parent and some parents are so damaged and in need of help themselves that they have little sense of what is and is not appropriate. Parents often do look to their children for what they more appropriately should be getting from adults. Sometimes society is very clear about this. When, for example, those needs are expressed sexually we term it sexual abuse and we are so sure that sexual relations between parents and children are not acceptable that we judge it a crime. But physical contact does not have to take place for the atmosphere in a house to be sexually charged in a damaging way. Few families are so comfortable with nakedness that they can walk around the house freely without some form of clothing. In our society children need bodily privacy and expect the same from their parents. When a father asks his teenage daughter to scrub his back in the bath or a mother repeatedly walks in on her teenage son while he's dressing, they can be crossing sexual boundaries with their children. Eventually a look, a tone of voice can have the same effect and be totally invisible to outsiders.

In a violent relationship the parent who is the victim of violence, usually the mother, may look to her children, particularly her sons, for protection. Depending on other factors, the effect can be devastating.[32] Boys can become protectors of women, getting involved in co-dependent relationships with women who are dependent on them or they can get lost in a confusing mix of conflicting emotions within themselves – self-loathing, anger, over-responsibility, hatred of one or both parents or guilt. The effect of domestic violence can be just as damaging to girls although they have a tendency to express it as withdrawal, self-mutilation, depression and caretaking – characteristics that don't attract as much attention as the acting out of boys.

Thankfully, this level of violence and inappropriate sexual contact are not found in the majority of families. In the average household inappropriate needs fulfilment by parents is less obvious and somewhat less damaging. The parent who looks to their child to be their best friend, to comfort them when they are worrying, to

91

be their confidante when trouble arises in the marriage or partnership, to praise them as a parent, to be their ambassador in the world, is inflicting a more subtle form of damage. The child's self-esteem can come to depend on their role in relation to the parent and they then take this role into their own adult life. They are valuable because they serve the needs of others. Their function in life is to help others.

Usually a parent is not aware that they are using their children in this way. They are fulfilling a need that wasn't met by their own parents and often they use the same methods their parents used on them. For example, when a teenage child stays out late the parent may be worried about them. This is par for the course as a parent. So is setting reasonable rules of behaviour, enforcing them and accepting the fact that your son or daughter won't like it and that they may tell you so loudly and clearly. Although it can be very difficult it is the parents' job to hold steady under this pressure, supporting each other when times get tough.

But if the parent feels alone or unsupported in other ways, they may take the defiance personally and may react by trying to make the child feel guilty. Guilt is a terrible burden for a child to carry. It's also a weapon that can easily be turned on parents. Other parents react to defiance by giving in on the rules in order to be popular with their child. This can teach the child manipulation, hinder the development of internal discipline, and, surprisingly, cause the child to feel unloved. I once asked my high-school English class what changes they would like to make in their parents. Much to my astonishment almost every one of the thirty-four fifteen-year-old girls wanted their parents to be firmer disciplinarians. And almost without exception they said that when a parent enforces the rules, no matter how much the child protests, it shows that they care and shows it far more than if they gave the child everything they wanted. In other words they wanted their parents to be parents, not friends, and they wanted the boundaries that would give them a feeling of security.

When a parent unloads their worries about money or their marriage on to their children, they are asking a child to assume responsibilities children are not equipped to shoulder. The child can become burdened with guilt and fear, constantly trying to think up ways to make things better for their parents. In the process, the child gets lost. Soon he learns to keep his opinions to himself or to comply with what others want even when it's against his own best interests.

Exercises

Sometimes it is hard to remember or recognise the way we fulfilled our parents' needs and perhaps there is no need to remember. What we need is awareness of our own feelings and behaviour so that we can grow in the present. The following exercises can be applied to your past as well as to your present relationships. The way we learned to relate as children is often reflected in our current relationships. Studying them can illuminate what happened when we were children.

1 The Role of a Lifetime
A role is a part we play in our lives in much the same way as an actor plays a part on stage. Ideally we act out many roles, choosing the one that is most appropriate in a given situation. But sometimes we get stuck in one or two roles and can't seem to get out of them. If this is the case it may be because that was the way our parents wanted it and the way we got approval as children.

What roles do you play in your present relationships? What roles did you play in your original family? Were/are you:

- a **caretaker** who makes people feel better, solves problems, attracts needy people?
- a **scapegoat** who takes the blame, even when someone else is responsible?
- a **joker** who is the life of the party, always good-humoured and relied on for a laugh?
- a **rebel** who defies authority even when it damages you to do so?

- a **rock** who always knows what to do, never breaks down, is great in a crisis?
- an **achiever** who works hard, earns money, excels, takes on challenges?
- a **pleaser** who does whatever others want you to do, apologises a lot, won't rock the boat?
- a **lost child** who fades into the background, suppresses their personality so others can shine?

There are many other roles people play in relationships, families and groups and if your role is not mentioned add it to the list. If you feel stuck in one of these roles it may be because you assumed it as a way of being what your family of origin needed you to be, what your present spouse/partner/friends need you to be. If you feel limited by the role, perhaps you could use your awareness of it to begin changing things. Seek help if necessary.

2 Pushing Buttons

How do people push your buttons? How do they get you to do what they want you to do? Make a list of all the important people in your life right now including your children. For each person think of a situation where they want you to do or give them something you don't particularly want to do or give. Or they want you to stop saying or doing something they don't like. How do they convince you? Do they:

- cry?
- flatter you?
- shout and bully?
- humiliate you in public?
- tell you you're wrong?
- be nice to you?
- other ways not mentioned here?
- tell you how much you're hurting them?
- compare you to others?
- seem helpless?
- reason with you?
- use put downs?
- show affection?

Find what works with you. This may be one of the methods your parents used. The important thing is to be aware that you don't have to respond. You can watch someone cry, sympathise and stick to your guns. Because someone tells you you're wrong it doesn't mean you *are* wrong and because someone is nice to you it doesn't mean you have to do what they want.

94

The Invisible Man – or Woman

Every child is a person. They are not adults in training, they are full human beings. Their abilities, both physical and mental, may not be those of an adult, but they have preferences, opinions, skills, abilities and choices that need to be seen and respected. The two extremes of parenting are the Victorian, where children are seen and not heard and all decisions are made for them, and the *laissez-faire* where few guidelines or rules are established and the child is involved in every decision the family must make. Somewhere in the middle is a balance between recognising the right of the child to have control over his own life and the child's need to learn how to live with others in a spirit of give and take. It is a difficult balance to achieve but getting it right is easier when parents really *see* their children as they are, rather than what they want their children to be. Adults who don't see children for who they are do things like making them kiss other adults when the child obviously doesn't want to, or make decisions for them even when the child is at an age when they could make those decisions for themselves.

Children who aren't really seen are often defined by their abilities or the roles they play out in the family. Children themselves tend to take on these roles. It's a sure-fire way of winning approval from parents, teachers and friends. Johnny is good at football. His talent is praised, talked about, boasted about to others. This sounds good and it is good for Johnny's self-esteem. But if being good at football is all people see in him, then the complex, multifaceted individual that Johnny is goes into hiding and gets lost. And when he tries to be more than a brilliant footballer, his desires can be dismissed or disapproved of. The depression and loneliness of the child who is strong and capable is often not seen and, when it is expressed, it can sometimes be trivialised or dismissed by adults who don't want to recognise it.

It is important to be seen so that we know who we are and get used to living with all aspects of ourselves. The child who isn't seen learns that certain aspects of himself are acceptable and others aren't, and if this happens he can miss out on the enjoyment of being who he wants to be from moment to moment. The child who isn't seen can learn that he is not important and should defer to the wishes of others. Such a child will not go for what he wants in life. And if all his decisions are made for him he can feel powerless and begin to wonder what's the point?

Exercise

The Face Behind the Mask
Make a list of all the talents and abilities you show to the world – and then list the ones you keep secret.

Specific Difficulties

The above are only some of the major categories in which parenting can be discussed and examined. Major events in a child's life not mentioned here can have profound effects on the way he sees himself and the world. The death of a parent or significant person in his young life can leave scars that last a long time, sometimes a lifetime. So can instances of emotional, sexual or physical abuse. The significance of major illnesses, traffic accidents, fires and other trauma is often dismissed, particularly if they happen early in a child's life, but is frequently recalled in rebirthing sessions. The reading list at the end of this book should guide you into further exploration of these and other areas.

Parents and Guilt

Parents often have similar reactions to the effects of their parenting as mothers do to birth. They often carry around a huge burden of guilt in relation to their children's upbringing. Guilt is not just a mill-stone around your neck and your child's it's also a waste of time. It doesn't protect your child and it doesn't undo anything.

David Chamberlain says it very eloquently: 'When children do something wrong, distraught parents take the blame and wonder what they have done wrong. The answer to that question is probably "nothing". You are only one of many forces converging on the life of your child.'[33] Rather than feeling guilty and acting out of that feeling, try to find the support you need to do your very difficult job more easily.

8
✿

The Eye of the Beholder

'There is nothing either good or bad
but thinking makes it so.'
[William Shakespeare, *Hamlet*, Act 2 Scene 2]

Most rebirthers would agree that we are damaged not so much by
what happens to us, but by the conclusions we draw from those
life events. Two people can have almost identical potentially
damaging experiences, yet the effect can be very different for each
of them. Things that appear devastating to an onlooker can leave
us unscathed while something that seems insignificant can have
life-long effects. Most of us can remember a casual remark made
by a parent or other significant person that stung us to the core.
That same person could have beaten us, shouted at us or otherwise
abused us on several occasions, but it was that one remark, often
not even directed at us, that we carry with us for the rest of our
lives. It is not what is said or done so much as what we make of
it that counts.

The Personal Law or Basic Mistake

When we begin this process of interpreting what happens to us and
drawing meaning from it, we lay the foundations of what rebirthers
call personal laws. These are very similar to what psychotherapist

Alfred Adler categorised as 'basic mistakes' but I prefer the term core beliefs*. These are very deeply engrained belief systems that influence almost every aspect of our lives. They can be life enhancing: 'I'm loveable' or 'life is easy', for example, or they can be much more limiting. Some of the more destructive core beliefs are:

- life is a struggle;
- I'm not wanted;
- I'll never make it;
- I'm worthless (unless I take care of others/succeed/love/ suffer/fail/am famous/etc.);
- Men/women abandon or hurt me;
- I hurt men/women;
- I'm insignificant/unimportant/powerless;
- I'm wrong.

These beliefs form very early – in the womb, at birth, or in infancy when the child was wide open to the world and its influences – and most people live under the sway of several such beliefs at the same time. They are like sense memories, convictions, vibrations in the body and they usually carry a strong emotional punch that reinforces the belief as well as making it very difficult to face. They may be just beneath the level of our awareness, or we may be fully conscious of them, but because they're not the sort of thing the average person chats about over lunch or a quiet drink, they go unchallenged. We accept them unquestioningly and take them to be the absolute truth of our existence, of human existence. They are, simply, the way things are. And they influence every area of our lives. Let's look at how this operates in the life of one man.

* For a more detailed explanation of Adler's theories see Adler, Alfred, *Social Interest*, 1998.

Nobody Listens

One of Dave's core beliefs is that he is powerless. This may have formed originally at birth when he was pulled from the birth canal with forceps and it could have been reinforced throughout Dave's childhood, perhaps by being bullied in school. Below is a diagram of how this particular belief operates in his life.

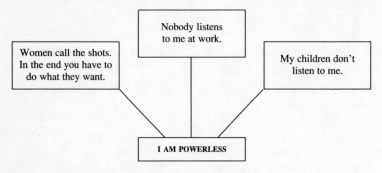

Core Belief and its Influence on Life

Dave's belief in his own powerlessness may be buried beneath the level of his awareness but, as the diagram shows, variations on the theme can be found littering his adult life. Because he doesn't recognise or own up to his own feelings of powerlessness, he projects them outwards on to the significant people in his life. In his relationship with his wife or partner, for example, he could feel she dominates, makes all the decisions and doesn't listen to him. This is a very common complaint among some men. In Dave's case it may or may not be true, but it's how Dave sees it and how he sees it becomes his reality. In relation to his family, the natural rebelliousness and contempt of his teenage children can feel like a complete loss of authority to him, and at work he may feel un-noticed and walked on. In this way a core and buried belief exercises a powerful influence throughout every major aspect of his life.

100

Self-fulfilling Prophecy

The self-fulfilling prophecy is the next step after the development of the core belief. This principle is probably best known in the field of education. If a school divides the students in any given year into classes labelled A to F (or some other hierarchical labelling system) with A perceived as the most intelligent and F at the opposite end of the scale, the students in the A class will tend to perform better than the students in the F class – regardless of their true level of intelligence. It is the belief in their own abilities, symbolised by the A on the classroom door and the expectations of teachers and parents – also heavily influenced by the A on the door – that count.

The same is true for all the beliefs we hold inside us. What we believe with conviction and emotional weight, we give rise to in our lives, like a prophecy that fulfils itself. The process is shown in the following diagram.

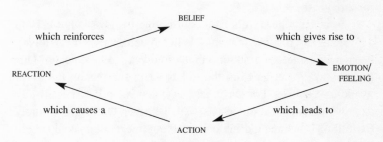

The Self-fulfilling Prophecy

Our core belief, when activated by a person or situation, gives rise to a feeling. Sometimes this feeling is so strong and arises so quickly after the activation of a belief, that it's difficult to separate the two. We may not be aware of the belief but we feel the feeling strongly and often act on it. And the action we take often causes a reaction in others that directly reinforces the original belief. In other words we prove ourselves right. Let's go back to Dave.

Dave has been working in the same job for several years without a pay rise. After thinking long and hard he decides to ask his boss for one. He rehearses his speech carefully and it sounds fine. But up to eighty per cent of our communication is non-verbal. The message we give out to others is in the way we hold our body, our physical gestures and in what used to be called 'vibes' – the sense we get of other people almost as soon as we meet them. These are things we find very difficult to control and they usually betray the truth about how we really feel no matter how brave or confident we sound. Dave has given himself several pep talks on how much he deserves a pay rise and how valuable he is to the company, but he approaches his boss with the underlying conviction that he is powerless to get what he wants in life. This belief is so old and so deeply ingrained in him that it will override any number of pep talks. He may have all the right words but what are the 'vibes' that Dave gives out to her boss when he walks into her office to ask for a pay rise?

If an event – in Dave's case confronting his boss – is likely to activate in any real way a painful belief system, then a diversionary behaviour, belief or emotion comes into play very quickly. This happens to protect us from the full brunt of the feeling the event would arouse in us. For Dave, this diversion is likely to be self-pity and resentment, but could just as easily be anger. Or he might simply reach for a cigarette, a drink or something to eat. He may also hold his breath or change his breathing pattern in some way. Any of these would act as a barrier between Dave and his powerlessness because they are easier to live with than the despair, self-loathing and pain that comes with believing we are weak and totally ineffectual in life. But asking for a rise while you exude anger, self-pity or resentment is more likely to annoy the boss than to persuade her to part with her precious cash. Dave may ask in a timid, whining or angry voice with body language to match. The likely result is that he will be fobbed off with some excuse. He has been ignored again as he knew he would be. The belief has become reality but Dave doesn't realise the key role he played in shaping that reality.

Something similar may be happening in Dave's relationship with his wife. She may really be the one who makes all the decisions and tells him what to do. This could be a personality trait she developed long before she met Dave. That pre-existing trait may have been reinforced over years of living with a man who gives in under the slightest resistance. If Dave believes he is powerless and thinks women are domineering and always win out in the end, there's not much point in making any kind of a decision his wife will disagree with. So he doesn't, or he gives in when she argues with him. She ends up making the decisions, getting her own way and Dave, once again, fulfils his own prophecy.

The relationship ends up in a circle that is hard to break out of. His wife's strength and decisiveness might have been the very qualities that attracted him to her in the first place. His dependence on her strength is what keeps him in the relationship. He blames her and all women but he needs her to give his life direction. And because she provides that direction he is never forced to look at his own core belief systems and the problems they are causing in his life.

A Key to Fit Every Lock

Dave's wife is caught in a similar trap. She may have a strong need to be in control, the product of a violent childhood perhaps, or a series of bad relationships. To her, Dave's willingness to listen to her opinion and defer to her wishes would have been very attractive in the heady days of falling in love. But over the years it has become tiresome and leaves her feeling isolated and alone in her responsibility for taking care of the family. Like her husband, instead of owning up to her need for control she blames him and the weakness of all men. As long as she believes men are weak and will let her down she will continue to make all the decisions in the family. And, as long as she makes all the decisions, her husband will have no encouragement or incentive to take on more responsibility. She too fulfils her own prophecy.

This dynamic is common in most relationships. We are attracted to people who fit our beliefs about ourselves, others and life, although it may not appear that way at first. In fact the beginning of a relationship may hold out the glittering promise of a new start with a person who is totally different from anyone we have known before. Caught up in the magic of falling in love we don't notice that while we may have changed our partner, we ourselves have not changed, and neither have our core beliefs. Months, maybe years later we realise with shock and often despair that we have repeated the same old pattern yet again. And quite often we do what we've always done – blame the other person.[34] This pattern applies in varying degrees of intensity to all relationships including friendships, relationships with children, colleagues and acquaintances. Breaking the pattern depends on looking inwards towards our own unresolved issues, not on changing the people around us. But to resolve our own issues it is helpful to look more closely at what happens when our core beliefs are activated, at what rebirthers call the make-wrong mechanism.

The Make-wrong Mechanism

The Make-wrong Mechanism underpins the dynamic of the self-fulfilling prophecy. Put simply, the make-wrong mechanism means that we believe we are a certain way, we label this unacceptable or wrong and then we decide that we must be different from the way we believe we are.

- I am ugly.
- I am wrong.
- I'm not good enough.
- Ugly is not the way to be.
- Being wrong is wrong.

- Not measuring up is wrong.
- I must be beautiful.
- I must be right.
- I must be better.

104

Albert Ellis, the founder of rational emotive therapy, called this '*must*urbation'* and when we apply it, as we do, to hundreds of situations every day it can cause a great deal of unnecessary pain. The pain comes, not so much from believing we are ugly, wrong, not good enough and so forth, but from making those character- istics wrong or unacceptable. We may have been taught to do that very early in life and are supported in doing it by society, but we are the ones condemning ourselves over and over again every day. And because making wrong generates so much pain, we often create additional problems for ourselves by trying to suppress the pain or push out of our awareness the original belief that we are flawed. We are trying to restore what Sigmund Freud called 'pleasure'.

These are the diversionary behaviours mentioned above in the case of Dave. Some people have constructed very complex and often self-destructive behaviour patterns and personality traits to keep these core beliefs unconscious. The particular pattern or trait people use depends on a host of other factors including the values that dominate the family of origin. If, for example, parents value worldly success, a child who believes he's not wanted may become an achiever as a way of running away from his core belief, and pleasing his parents at the same time. If the family or the social climate of the times emphasises being good, helpful, saving the world, the child may become a carer or chronically 'nice' to everyone. In fact diversionary behaviour can be anything from addictions or com- pulsions to self-pity destructiveness, chronic anger or depression.

The pattern could best be described as a pendulum where we are constantly swinging between two extremes with our diver- sionary behaviours in the middle, easing the pain, making us feel better. But always there are the moments when the diversion doesn't work. The workaholic finds himself without work for the

* For an exploration of Ellis's theories, see Ellis, Albert, *Humanistic Psychotherapy: The Rational Emotive Approach*, NY, Julian Press and McGraw-Hill Paperbacks, 1973.

two weeks of his holidays and feels lost, uneasy, irritable. The dieter weakens and eats the bar of chocolate. The carer meets someone who can take care of themselves, the alcoholic sobers up and finds the world a cold and dismal place. When that happens we are right back into feeling bad again, often without knowing why. Then the swing to the other side begins all over again.

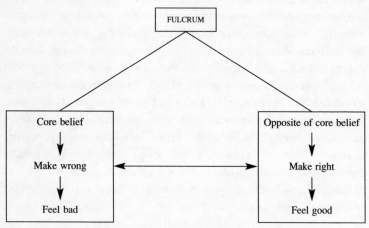

Attempts to avoid feeling the pain of the core belief
e.g. eating, smoking, addictions, anger, shyness, blame,
withdrawal, alterations of the breathing pattern,
compulsions, self-pity, niceness, service to others, etc.

The Make-wrong Mechanism

Getting to the fulcrum in a dilemma is something that happens a lot in rebirthing. In many ways it is similar to the Buddhist koan. We are presented with a problem to which we can see only a limited number of possible solutions, often only the two opposites. But in a non-ordinary state of consciousness we can find a non-ordinary perspective on our problem. We move outside it, beyond it, and from this vantage point what once loomed so large in our lives often becomes totally irrelevant.

The Perks

Another aspect of the diversionary behaviour is that it often gets us the attention we crave or it helps us feel important and of value in life. This is called a secondary benefit. It is often allied to a very tenaciously held belief that our needs must be met by other people – one of the most dangerous *must*urbations of all. The secondary benefit can exercise such a strong pull on us that change becomes very difficult. But the almost addictive need for attention or a sense of importance in life can be valuable signposts on our inward journey. They can point us to the fulcrum of our pendulum where we know in our bones that we are of value simply because we exist, or we learn to be so in touch with our core selves that the attention of others becomes irrelevant. For some people, letting go of the secondary benefit and of their belief that their needs must be fulfilled by others, can be confusing and frightening. There can be relapses along the way which are discouraging. In this case it is important to proceed slowly and gently and get help from an understanding and supportive rebirther.

Another Cinderella Story

Anna came to me for rebirthing because she suffered from chronic shyness and never had a relationship that lasted longer than a few dates. Anna had above average looks, good skin, hair and eyes. She was a little overweight but it made her look voluptuous rather than fat. But, in spite of all this, she believed she was ugly to the point of being repulsive. To help her cope with the pain of this she comfort ate and spent lots of time reading and watching TV instead of taking some exercise and going out and meeting people. The result of course was that she put on weight: the self-fulfilling prophesy. Anna's pendulum looked like this (see over):

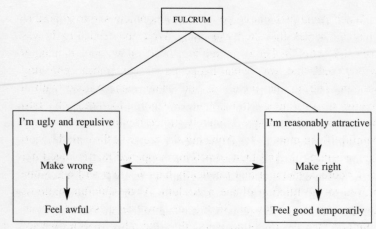

Dieting, shyness, self-pity, positive self-talk,
comfort eating, incomplete inhalation.

Anna's Make-wrong Mechanism

Throughout her life Anna had swung between the belief in her own
ugliness and its opposite. She had spurts of dieting and exercise
which got her to a shape she could accept. But the core belief was
still lurking in the background dooming her to failure. She stayed
slim for a few months at most and then fell back to the old pattern
of comfort eating. And each time she put weight back on she felt
worse about herself. She was beginning to suffer from depression.

Socially Anna was a classic case of the self-fulfilling prophesy.
Her friends could see it clearly and told her so. At parties she hung
out alone in the corner holding a drink and hoping nobody would
notice her. When men did approach her she thought they were
either feeling sorry for her or making fun of her in some way.
Either way, she couldn't keep eye contact with them and found any
excuse to get away. They interpreted this as 'she's not interested
in me' and quickly moved on to someone else. She saw this as
confirmation that she was repulsive, dull and boring. Her beliefs
shaped her reality and her reality reinforced her beliefs.

When Anna first started personal development she tried hard to convince herself that she wasn't ugly. What she needed to do was face the belief in her own ugliness head on without making it wrong, and that was what happened in her fourth rebirthing session. During the breathing she came face to face with a revulsion so strong she thought she was going to vomit. This part of the session lasted approximately fifteen minutes. It was a very painful fifteen minutes for Anna but she breathed through the feeling, accepting it. And then something happened that changed her to her core, something that frequently happens in rebirthing. Anna moved to the fulcrum of the pendulum. At the fulcrum ugliness and beauty are irrelevant. So too are powerlessness and power, unimportance and importance and all of the other dualities we see as essential in our lives. What matters is that we are who we are in any given moment without judgement. In Anna's case this meant that she could look in the mirror and for the first time in her life see what other people saw – a reasonably attractive woman who looked better on some days than on others. Her self-esteem no longer depended on her appearance or what other people thought of it. This was a situation Anna could live with quite happily.

*Mus*turbating Life Away

This make-wrong mechanism, this '*mus*turbation' doesn't just apply to the fundamental core beliefs but to the hundreds of often insignificant issues that fill our daily lives. Many of our difficulties in living come not from the wrong circumstances, but from making the circumstances wrong. Combine this with our conviction that things or people must, should or ought to be different and we have a recipe for pain and discontent.

An example: My boss is abrupt and rude and her gruff manner offends me. Why? Because not saying please and thank you, not making polite conversation damages me physically and emotionally? Or because I think my boss *should* be polite because I've been brought up to believe that's the way people *ought* to be. If they're not, it means they don't respect me and people *should* respect me. So because I think my boss doesn't respect me, I get offended and hurt and think about leaving. But things could be different. Take away the insistence that my boss should be polite to me and I will simply get on with my job and ignore her manner. I might even find that if I am not disapproving and offended all the time I might actually get to know and like my boss. Either way, life will be a lot easier.

My relationship with my boss is generally not a life-threatening situation. But in more serious circumstances this obsession with must, should and ought can become a deeply damaging tyranny. Take for example a situation of domestic violence. Many things combine to keep women – and men – in violent relationships: terror, intimidation, low self-esteem, no place to go, money, children, etc. But one element is '*must*urbation'. Many women, particularly in the early stages, spend a lot of time stunned by the fact that the husband or partner who should love them is actually abusing them. It often takes a long time to face the reality that what *should* be true, isn't. The loving, happy relationship that *should* last a lifetime is violent and abusive. And in the months or years it takes to overcome this particular 'must', all concerned can be injured, killed or emotionally scarred.

Letting go of the 'must', getting to the fulcrum where facts are just facts, frees the mind to think more clearly. It would be very nice if things were different and in an ideal world they would be, but they're not. Our attachment to what *should* be, and to working out why it isn't that way, paralyses us into inactivity and, like picking at an open wound, it greatly increases our pain. Reality is reality and our job is to decide how we want to deal with it. When this becomes clear, the means of achieving our goal tends to fall into place. This is a form of *synchronicity*, the world supporting a clear and heartfelt intention.

But if the basic belief system is not resolved we tend to repeat our behaviour and find ourselves in the same situations, the same kind of relationships over and over again. Freud described this as the repetition compulsion syndrome – the compulsion to re-enact what we could not resolve the first time it happened to us. Rebirthers categorise the repetition compulsion, the phenomenon of synchronicity, together with the concept of the self-fulfilling prophesy under the umbrella heading of 'thought is creative'.

Exercises

For these exercises you will need a pen, paper and, if possible, a good friend. Some people may find the first exercise difficult to do because it can go to the core of who we believe we are. While all of the exercises can be done as private personal-development work, I recommend that you use them in conjunction with rebirthing sessions with a trained rebirther.

1 Discovering Core Beliefs

Find a quiet place where you won't be disturbed. Have paper and pen handy. Sit comfortably, close your eyes and take a few deep breaths. Focus your attention on your breathing and the world within yourself. Then open your eyes and write down all the negative beliefs you have about yourself. Do it quickly without thinking about it. It doesn't matter if they don't make sense. Keep writing until nothing more comes to you. Now review your list and find one that has an emotional charge for you. Turn this into an affirmation (see chapter 13) and work with it.

2 Core Beliefs in Action

Pick a situation or relationship in your life with which you are not satisfied, not getting your basic needs met. (Start with one which you think might be relatively easy to resolve.) Describe in writing what you do in this situation: your body movements, your breathing patterns, physical sensations, what you say, how much eye contact you make, etc. You might be able to get a friend to help you with this. Then try to slow the picture down. What are you feeling? And lastly, what are you thinking? What are the programmes playing in your mind at this time?

Write these down. Then see if you can find another bottom line below what you are thinking at this time. For example, if you are thinking 'They don't like me', is your bottom line really 'I'm not likeable'? It may be difficult to do this at first but, with practice, awareness becomes more detailed.

3 *Mus*turbation

Begin a list of 'shoulds' for yourself. At the top of the page write 'I should . . .' and without thinking too much about it complete the sentence until no more shoulds come to you. You can use various categories such as your body, place in the world, relationships, money, etc. Then you can move on to other people should, the world should, the government should and so forth. Some examples are:

BODY	PLACE IN WORLD	OTHER PEOPLE
I should be thinner.	I should have a better job.	X should make me happy.
I should get fit.	I should be making a difference.	X should support me.
I should have a flat stomach.	I should be helping people more.	People should be nicer.
I should be taller.	I should be an executive by now,	People should be fair.

When you have completed your list here are some questions to answer about it:

- Where did you get these beliefs from?
- Are they really yours?
- Do you believe you should live up to them?
- If you should be this perfect, should everyone else live up to the same standards?
- Do you have one standard for yourself and another for other people?
- Is it reasonable to expect anyone to be that perfect?
- Is it humanly possible for anyone to be that perfect?

9

Empowerment

'Life is a mirror that gives back as much as it receives.'
[Evan S Connell, *Mrs Bridge*]

What do you do when someone hurts you? I know I run little scenarios over and over again in my head – the scene as it happened, the scene as it might have happened – trying to convince myself that I was right and the other person was wrong. I also get angry. Anger is quite a normal reaction to being hurt. When a child is hurt by another child, that anger is given expression. They may hit back, there's probably some crying, they run to mother and ten minutes later they are happily playing again. What the child has done is complete a cycle. His emotions have been aroused and expressed, and in expression they find resolution. In showing his anger, the child is also displaying the hurt that give rise to it and he has few inhibitions about crying and complaining about the pain. As adults we know we can't give vent to anger the way children do. There would be chaos in society and we would probably end up in jail. Most of us don't feel comfortable exposing the fact that we've been hurt. Revealing raw wounds leaves us vulnerable and is not always a wise thing to do in certain circumstances. Instead we use a variety of means, including holding our breath, to suppress our feelings.

But what if the damage is really deep, the kind that stems from birth or childhood or from physical injury, abuse or rape? Perhaps you've been hurt by a spouse or partner, a parent, friend or someone you really trusted. Dealing with this is much more complex than the way a child deals with his toy being taken by another child. It can be difficult to cope with the strong energy of anger and the pain of being hurt in this way. Diversionary tactics come to our rescue. One of these is resentment which often leads to blame.

Blaming is a feature of our society and culture. We learn to blame very early in life. When a young child bumps into a table and hurts himself, the first thing an adult does is slap the table and say, 'Bad table!'. The child has done something we might call silly; he has bumped into a stationary object and caused himself pain. There is nothing wrong with being silly and bumping into the table, although unpleasant it will teach him something about spatial relations and co-ordination. But adults have learned that being silly is somehow wrong. In the same situation they would feel very uncomfortable, so they jump in to save the child from embarrassment that the child himself may not feel. That simple act of slapping the table teaches the child that making a mistake is wrong, something to be ashamed of and hidden from view. It also teaches him to blame others for things that happen to him. When this lesson is repeated throughout our childhood it can become so much a part of who we are that we no longer recognise it.

Anything or anybody can be blamed for an endless range of life's problems and difficulties: friends, neighbours, family, God, rich people, poor people, men, women, spouses, partners, politicians, the churches, the other side in a conflict . . . the list is endless. As a rebirther I have found that blame is most often laid at the feet of parents and spouses, but what surprises clients is that their heaviest load of blame is usually reserved for themselves.

114

What is Blame?

Sometimes people have difficulty taking credit for their achieve-ments. Occasionally phrases like 'I didn't do anything, Johnny or Mary did all the work' is false modesty, but quite often people genuinely believe others did the work that made their achievements possible. This is attributing responsibility for an event in our life to forces outside ourselves. When that event or situation is painful or limiting, apportioning sole responsibility for it to forces outside ourselves is called blame.

People can be deeply hurt in relationships with others. The wounds can take a long time to heal and blame is often a stage in the develop-mental process of healing and growth. When people are hurt they often seek retribution. Their pain, they believe, will not be eased until the person who hurt them is punished. In cases of serious crime this may mean a prison sentence. In more personal matters it often means forcing the offending person to recognise the repercussions of their actions. Gaining a criminal conviction against an abuser or murderer may be part of the recovery process for the people affected by his or her actions, but a criminal conviction may never come to pass. The friend who we believe betrayed us, the parent who humiliated us in public, the spouse who beats us may never see or admit to the effects of their actions. Even if they do, the pain and the damage are still there and have to be lived with on a daily basis.

Pinning everything on the punishment of the 'perpetrator' distracts the 'victim' from focusing on the pain they feel. Blaming others puts the process of recovery, the power to change our life circumstances, into the hands of another person. It makes us help-less and dependent on the person or people we believe caused our problem in the first place. It is supremely disempowering.

Working Things Through

There are many stages to working through personal issues. Some people have been so traumatised by events that they have blotted out all memory of what happened. Others remember but find it difficult to really acknowledge that they have been hurt. They are so close to the person who they perceive has hurt them – a trusted parent, spouse, uncle, aunt or grandparent perhaps – that they can't step back and see that person as a separate individual. This separation process is very important in recovery and blame may play a role in it.

This acknowledgement of what happened can unleash anger that may have been bottled up for years. If we're not used to feeling it, anger can be a very unpleasant emotion. If we don't know how to express it, it can also be very destructive. Most of the clients I have worked with have passed through this stage with an adequate level of self-control and reason. We discuss their feelings in depth but they know instinctively that lashing out is neither appropriate nor helpful, particularly if it is against people who have always done the best they could in raising their children.

Behind the anger and blame lies hurt. Coming to terms with this can be very painful, but until it is faced, it can't be resolved. This is the stage where, in my experience, people pull back from blame and begin to focus on themselves. And in focusing on themselves they begin to feel the first tentative stirrings of their own personal power. Personal power, that sense of being in charge of your own life, of being able to shape your own experience and direction, begins with taking responsibility for your reactions to what has transpired in your life.

Rebirthing is a particularly effective technique to use throughout this process, but I have found that at this point it is invaluable. Strong feelings can be experienced and resolved quickly through the breath. And they are resolved, not skipped over. At the same time the emergence of the rebirthee's own personal power is experienced in a way that touches all levels of his or her existence – mind, body, spirit and emotions.

Once the blame, the anger and a lot of the pain have been taken out of the picture, patterns often begin to emerge. People begin to see the many, often very subtle ways in which they have contributed to their own experience. They become aware of core beliefs and how those beliefs informed their actions and reactions. They also begin to recognise how their own actions and reactions have shaped their lives.

This is *self-responsibility* and with it lies the power to consciously shape future experience. When people reach this stage they cease to blame others. The anger, bitterness and resentment they once felt melts away, often without their realising this has happened. This is often called forgiveness and, unlike blame, it is supremely empowering.

It is important to remember that this is developmental work. It is a growth process that develops in stages over time. Rebirthing can greatly speed it up, but, in my experience, it can't be forced and the stages of the process can't be skipped. When I first started rebirthing it was popular to focus on forgiveness and rebirthers recommended what was called a 'forgiveness diet', an extensive affirmation technique developed by Sondra Ray. For me, the effect was to superficially skim over a process that needed time, honesty and acceptance to help it develop organically. Forgiveness is what happens of its own accord when issues are resolved and pain has been worked through. One of the dangers of 'trying' to forgive someone is that the person who has been hurt will misunderstand the concept of self-responsibility and will blame themselves for 'creating' the situation in which other people hurt them. Because I believe forgiveness is a developmental process there are no exercises at the end of this chapter.

PART 3

THE JOURNEY

Chapters 4–9 explain the basic components of one of the maps that goes with rebirthing. Rebirthers explain it and express it in different ways. They use many styles and techniques culled from various sources and devised by themselves to facilitate understanding and insight. And the map is important. It satisfies the part of us that needs explanations, that needs to understand what we are experiencing. It is useful and comforting when navigating unfamiliar terrain.

But as Kylea Taylor points out, the map is not the territory. The core of rebirthing, the place where the most fundamental movement and resolution take place, is in the period of the session devoted to conscious connected breathing. Once the breathing session begins, the psychological map ceases to be of any great importance. The breath puts the rebirthee in the middle of the terrain with their own breathing as the only guide they need.

This section of the book looks at what actually happens once a person begins to breathe in the rebirthing manner. Chapter 10 describes, in so far as it is possible to describe it in words, the elements of rebirthing, the components of the experience. Chapter 11 will go into this strange and wonderful journey in greater detail. We will then look at how rebirthing can help you manage stress in your daily life and how you can use the technique to help you to enhance your creativity and live more creatively.

Rebirthing has to be experienced to be fully understood. It is unlikely that you will be able to rebirth yourself from reading this part of the book and I don't recommend you try. The first few sessions should be done with a trained rebirther who can provide the support and encouragement most people need to engage fully in the process. After you have completed a few sessions, enough to feel at ease with using your breath, you can begin working with the technique at home as well as going for sessions. These chapters can then become a guide to the process.

10

☯

How Rebirthing Happens

'[Rebirthing] is a journey from what you think
you are, through who you fear you might be, to
who you really are.'
[*Breathe* July, August, September 1992]

When I first started working as a rebirther I used to hold free
introductory meetings in my home. Usually at least one person who
attended the meeting became a client and so, flushed with success,
I was keen to attract even greater numbers from each session. I
worked very hard on my speech, trying to cover all the angles, tell
them everything they could possibly expect if they decided to
begin rebirthing. I told them about all the physical sensations, the
euphoria, the resolving of old baggage, the incredible energy, the
emotions, the sense of connection to the world . . . everything I had
experienced and everything everyone I knew had experienced. My
speech got longer and longer and I was very pleased with myself.
The last introductory meeting I held produced one client who went
on to do a series of sessions very successfully and profitably for
him. On his last session, when we were reviewing and saying
goodbye, he asked me if I remembered the introductory meeting
where he had asked so many questions. I remembered it well. I had
given my finest speech ever. 'You know all that stuff you told us
about rebirthing?' he asked. 'Yes,' I replied becoming cautious.
'Well none of it was true.'

I learned my lesson. Since then when people ask me what it is like to experience a rebirth I tell them a little of what it has been like for me and then I tell them that it may be similar for them but it could also be totally different. A rebirthing session is different for everyone, every time. This fact makes rebirthing hard to explain and what makes it even more difficult is that rebirthing is a non-ordinary experience. There are few reference points in everyday life to adequately explain what happens when a person lies down for an hour or so and breathes consciously and connectedly. The experience can be described in words and the reader will have some notion of what those words mean. But this, to paraphrase author Peter Hoeg, is like trying to describe music in words.[35] It can't really be done. Words paint a one-dimensional picture while the experience of rebirthing is multi-dimensional, comprehensive, involving all the senses and faculties at once. That said, there are certain aspects of the rebirthing process that can be explained.

The Five Elements

Many writers on the subject describe rebirthing as having five basic elements. These five elements form the structure of a session and on this structure can be hung an infinite variety of experience all generated by the individual client. It could be likened to ten different architects who have all been given the same core steel structure for a building. Using their unique experience, training and point of view they will produce ten very different looking finished products but all will be built upon a similar frame. The five basic elements of rebirthing are:

- conscious connected breathing;
- total relaxation;
- awareness in detail;
- total acceptance;
- whatever happens is part of the process.

These elements are listed in order for the purposes of description and sometimes they follow each other in that order. But generally all five elements come into operation at once or in no particular pre-set order. They overlap and run into each other and form part of a wonderful holistic experience.

Conscious Connected Breathing

The breathing of rebirth is *conscious* because both rebirther and rebirthee focus their attention on every stage of the inhale and exhale. What is normally done unconsciously is now done with full awareness and when we become conscious of breathing we find that what seems like a simple one-step event expands into a very pleasurable, multi-dimensional experience. There is the feeling of air coming in through the nostrils or mouth, the effect the air has on the hairs in the nose or on the tongue, the smooth passage down through the throat and then the intense, mildly ticklish contentment of the lungs slowly filling. Following this the sensation of the lungs emptying, then the second of nothingness before the pleasure of inhale begins again. Becoming conscious of breathing in this detail is good practice for becoming conscious of the many details of the internal world that breathing will open up. Awareness of the process of breathing can also alert us to the many idiosyncrasies of our breathing which may mirror the way we are in life – our breath armouring.

This dual function of breathing can be seen throughout the rebirthing process. Our breathing is a reflection of our personality and we can learn a lot about ourselves from observing the way we take in and expel air. At the same time breathing offers us a way of resolving the issues that have shaped that personality and influenced the way we behave in the world.

Breath armouring is one of the reasons why the breathing is also *connected*. In rebirthing, connected breathing means there are no pauses during the inhale or exhale or between inhale and exhale. Breathing is one continuous, circular motion. As we've seen in

125

chapter 2, interruptions to the breathing mechanism can be used to keep strong emotions or painful belief systems at bay. As the rebirthee learns to breathe consciously and connectedly he smoothes out the kinks in his normal pattern of inhale and exhale, gradually allowing these defences in his breathing to slip away. The result is a freeing of the breath and of the energy flowing through the body. The rebirthee embraces that which keeps him alive, life, the breath. When this happens some of the unresolved issues that the breath armouring kept suppressed can surface. This can take many forms including insights or other thoughts, emotions, visual images, physical or energetic sensations and memories. As the rebirthee continues to breathe consciously and connectedly, these experiences, often described simply as patterns of energy, come to full awareness and intensity. And then the breath takes the rebirthee through the intensity to resolution – or what rebirthers call integration. Resolution is usually followed by a period of calm contentment and rebalancing of energy in the body.

But within this broad sweep of the breath's journey are many interesting variations and curious details. For most rebirthees their breathing rhythm, depth and speed varies throughout the session in response to what they are experiencing. This often happens spontaneously when the body, mind and breath are working together. But rebirthing can bring up strong feelings. These need not always be what we call 'bad'. Intense joy, exuberance and peacefulness can be as much a part of the rebirthing process as sorrow, anger, anguish or fear. And for some people the 'good' emotions are almost as difficult to contain as the bad. When these feelings emerge the 'make-wrong mechanism' can come into play. The rebirthee, rejecting what he is feeling, can respond by returning to his normal daily breathing pattern or by breathing very fast and pushing out on the exhale. Should this happen the rebirther will encourage him to relax his breathing and let the exhale drop out like a sigh with nothing but the weight of his ribcage to push it.

This pushing away of feelings with a fast, forced exhale may be the breathwork counterpart to the rebirthee's reaction to difficulties in daily life. If he responds to situations and feelings he finds intense or undesirable by becoming anxious, panicky and pushing them away, this is an opportunity for him to deal with this pattern as it is reflected in his breathing. Slower, more relaxed breathing brings a more relaxed, accepting state of mind and allows him to integrate the material that has been activated. At the same time he may discover that his habitual responses are not necessarily the best way to deal with stressful situations. Accepting his feelings and using his breath to reach resolution is much easier and more productive.

The rebirther interferes as little as possible in the breathing session of their client. However, it is the rebirther's job to monitor the breathing and make suggestions that facilitate ease of integration. Fast, forced breathing is only one variation in breathing that can happen in rebirthing. Some others are listed below together with possible reasons for the change and the suggestions a rebirther may make during the session.

PATTERN	POSSIBLE EFFECT/REASON	SUGGESTIONS
Fast and forced	Uncomfortable material activated	More relaxed breathing
Full and fast	Activation of (pleasurable) material	Not applicable
Full and slow	Activation and integration	Not applicable
Shallow and fast	Integration of (difficult) material	Not applicable unless exhale is forced
Slow and shallow	Drowsiness	Fast and full breathing
Shallow, at normal pace	Early in session – reluctance to enter the process End of session – blissfulness	Deeper breathing Not applicable
Forced exhale	Controlling what is activated, fear	Relax the exhale
Pauses	Controlling, holding back, fear	Circular breathing

Variations in Breathing

127

It is important to note that a breathing pattern that could indicate reluctance or rejection early in a session could be an expression of blissful contentment at the end. A well-trained and experienced rebirther can usually tell the difference. Because of this tendency to reject strong feelings when they arise, it is wise to learn rebirthing first by doing sessions with a rebirther. The rebirther acts as a breathing coach. They teach clients how to use their breath to deal with anything that might arise for them by varying the breath where appropriate or by focusing the breath into parts of the body where the rebirthee feels energetic intensity. There is no need to force anything in rebirthing, including the breath, and if people begin to struggle, the rebirther is there to encourage relaxation and gentleness. Conscious connected breathing is very easy to learn and as they get used to rebirthing, rebirthees are able to accept any emotions that may be activated and continue breathing appropriately. In this way the rebirthee learns to trust the process of breathing. When this happens they may experience a breath release.

Breath Release
A breath release is when the rebirthee surrenders completely to his own breath and it can feel as if he is being breathed rather than breathing. It is a wonderful experience of flowing with the breath, of giving over to it and letting it proceed as it will, knowing that it can be trusted completely to take the breather wherever they need to go safely.

Energy Release
An energy release often follows a breath release. Energy builds up in the body usually in the area of the feet or knees. This feels like tingling, flowing or a strong sense of intensity inside the body. This energy can be felt very clearly moving up through the body, growing in intensity, until it dissolves around the shoulders and head area. This can happen several times in succession and once the

rebirthee gets used to it an energy release becomes a very enjoyable experience.

Hyperventilation in Rebirthing

Hyperventilation, when defined as an uncontrolled breathing rhythm with a forced exhale, is not part of the rebirthing technique. The early stages of hyperventilation can sometimes happen in rebirthing, particularly when activated material is 'made wrong' (see pp. 104–11) or not fully accepted (see the fourth element, total acceptance). If this is happening, rebirthers usually ask the rebirthee to relax their exhale as soon as it becomes apparent that they are forcing air out of their lungs. However, some breathwork schools accept hyperventilation as a part of the process[36] and arguments rage about its usefulness as a therapeutic tool.

Tetany

Also known as alkalosis, tetany is a symptom of hyperventilation and occurs when the exhale is forced. The lower levels of carbon dioxide affect the acid-alkaline balance in the blood. This can lead to cramping of the muscles particularly in the hands (claw hands) and around the mouth. Tetany can be very painful but it is harmless and disappears quickly once the rebirthee relaxes his exhale. Tetany sometimes happens during rebirthing, especially in the early sessions before rebirthees have learned to accept everything that emerges without judgement. Opponents of the use of hyperventilation would see tetany as an undesirable phenomenon. Yet it can work very well for the benefit of the client. On his third session, one of my clients whose presenting complaint was emotional numbness, went into full-body tetany, much the same as in my first experience of rebirthing. Far from being dissatisfied, he said afterwards that for the first time in his life he had begun to feel. However, the majority of people go through rebirthing without ever experiencing tetany.

Upper-chest Breathing in Rebirthing

The emphasis in rebirthing has always been on upper-chest breathing. This means breathing into the area at the top of the lungs, beneath the collar bones. It is a part of the lungs we under-utilise and if people are used to belly breathing they can find this strange. It is important to emphasise that the kind of upper-chest breathing used in rebirthing is very different from the breathing that leads to hyperventilation. The upper-chest breathing I am talking about here emphasises the upper chest but involves the whole of the lungs. Gunnel Minett calls it 'super-breathing'.[37] Eventually it feels as if the whole body is breathing and it is accompanied by deep relaxation.

Nose and Mouth Breathing

In rebirthing, breathing can be either through the nose or the mouth. Nasal breathing in general tends to result in a more cerebral experience, mouth breathing tends to bring up emotions more intensely. If intense emotions are activated, mouth breathing allows a freer passage of a greater volume of air and is often more suitable to the integration of such feelings. Sometimes people switch over to nasal breathing when they feel dryness in their throat or mouth but this dryness disappears quickly if the rebirthee continues to focus on his breathing. It's not advisable to combine the two kinds of breathing – in through the nose and out through the mouth for example – as the quality of the experience tends to be mixed.

Total Relaxation

Relaxation is an important element in rebirthing. Physical relaxation begins with lying comfortably on a mattress or bed. Sometimes rebirthers play soft music and guide the client through the progressive relaxation of each part of their body before beginning the breathing session. The breathing itself can begin with the rebirthee simply becoming aware of his own breath, its rhythm and pace and the sensations in his body. As he feels comfortable he can begin to lengthen his inhale and bring the breath higher into his chest. It is important to proceed gently, relaxing, sinking into the breath as one would sink into a soft, enveloping feather bed. Once the rebirthee surrenders to the process of breathing, the body can become very deeply relaxed indeed and at the end of the session limbs can feel heavy and totally at ease. As the body relaxes and the breathing becomes automatic, the mind becomes still. Gradually the stresses and concerns of the day slip away and the rebirthee is free to become absorbed in the fascinating world inside himself.

This state of deep physical and mental relaxation allows the breath to do its work of activating suppressed emotions, thought patterns and sometimes memories. When this happens another kind of relaxation comes into play, a relaxation of attitude. When some difficult material emerges it will be resolved more easily and quickly if the rebirthee can maintain a relaxed attitude towards it, taking it in his stride without too much anxiety. This 'laid-back' attitude is the product of not making what emerges wrong and is closely connected with the fourth element, total acceptance.

Awareness in Detail

Many people who come to rebirthing complain that they don't know what they feel or want. Most people have had the experience of being thrown off balance in a situation, being swept into agreeing to something they don't actually agree with or allowing themselves to be walked on without realising what was happening. Afterwards they recognise what has transpired. They know they're feeling angry and they know what they should have said or done. But by then it is too late.

Part of the problem in both these cases is a lack of awareness of what we are really feeling and thinking in the moment. We spend much of our lives disconnected from what is going on inside us. The clutter of a busy life as well as all the diversionary behaviours mentioned in chapter 8 are ways of distracting

131

ourselves from our internal world. If we spend most of our day detached from our inner life, we will find it difficult to know our own desires and needs. We will also find it difficult to remain present to ourselves in situations where we really need to know what we are feeling and thinking.

A rebirthing session is a very good place to practise the kind of awareness that allows us to get to know ourselves again. A heightened sense of awareness is a feature of rebirthing and it begins with awareness of the breath. Each stage of the inhale and exhale is accompanied by subtle yet strong emotions and thought patterns. From the breath, awareness moves out to cover all the sensations, pains, aches, tingling and energy movements in the body. These are the kind of things we normally pay no attention to, but if we did they could alert us to the onset of stress and illness. As we linger on these energy patterns, awareness moves to the emotions and belief systems buried behind our coping mechanisms. The process is like peeling away layers of thoughts, feelings and physical sensations. As one layer comes away we find what is beneath it, and if we are willing to linger there, breathe and accept what happens without judgement, we move to the layer beneath that again. What we find has always been there, awareness simply brings it to the forefront.

Total Acceptance

Sometimes, when giving talks about rebirthing, I ask the audience to do the twenty connected breaths exercise described at the end of chapter 12. Each person has a different experience. Some describe it as very pleasant, relaxing, joyful. Others report heaviness in their chest, choking, feeling that the air is being sucked out of the room, anger or fear. All this can come about through twenty connected breaths. Some of those who experience strong reactions are impressed and want to go further. Others decide that because these feelings are unpleasant there must be something wrong or dangerous about rebirthing.

132

What the exercise has done is show them the power of their own breathing and given them a taste of what they are carrying around inside them every day of their lives. What they have done is make what they feel wrong. As a result they stop short of fully experiencing those feelings. And if we consistently avoid feeling our feelings we deny ourselves the opportunity to work through and resolve them. It is important in rebirthing not to pass judgement on anything we feel while we are breathing. Some people may experience localised physical pain, most people, at some stage, experience strong emotions. They may want to cry, shout or they may feel like thumping somebody. They may want to beat themselves up or feel self-revulsion so strong they want to vomit. These are the feelings they have been avoiding all their lives. Rebirthing gives them the opportunity to bring them into the open at last and be done with them.

But the minute we pass judgement on our feelings they go into retreat again. We need to accept everything about ourselves, including things we find unpleasant or even shameful. They are all part of who we are and rebirthing is a process of embracing every aspect of ourselves. There may be many elements of our behaviour that we want to change, but change is much easier and more lasting if we first embrace ourselves as we are, lovingly and without judgement.

A good example of this is the quiet child who is found in many classrooms. This child may be bright, studious and know all the answers to the teacher's questions but she never raises her hand or makes a contribution to class discussions. With the best intentions – or because they themselves are uncomfortable with silence – the teacher and the child's parents may encourage her to talk more. But the message the child is getting is that who she is, a quiet, possibly shy person, is wrong. If she is told this often enough she comes to reject her own quietness. But self-rejection doesn't make people more outgoing or confident. In fact it does the opposite. She grows even quieter. The solution is to accept her as she is, accept the very quality they find undesirable and allow her to be quiet if that is who she is. The likely effect is that the confidence and self-esteem that flourishes in the warmth of acceptance will free her from shyness and allow her to speak when she wants to.

The same is true in rebirthing. What we reject about ourselves sticks with us through all attempts to eradicate it. Embracing it has the opposite effect. Embracing and accepting everything that comes up for us in a rebirthing session allows us to breathe through it until we reach the point where it no longer has a hold over our lives. It doesn't matter whether this is a minor ache in our big toe, a particularly distressing memory of birth or an emotion flooding through our whole body. Accepting it allows it to integrate so we can move on to the layer beneath, eventually – and often quite quickly – reaching the joy and peace that is at the core of ourselves.

One of the cumulative effects of rebirthing is to realise that feelings aren't facts. In a rebirthing context this phrase, coined by Dr Abraham Low (the founder of the Recovery movement), means that feelings are simply energetic responses to the belief systems we hold inside us. They may appear overwhelming and all consuming. We may see them as solid, immutable reality on which we should rightly base our judgements and actions. But rebirthing shows that we can let feelings pass through us, watch ourselves feeling and move on to what is beyond. And feelings move on very quickly in rebirthing.

Whatever Happens is Part of the Process

Some rebirthing sessions are packed full of internal events. Some are calm and uneventful as if nothing were happening. Others are marked by dogs barking, trucks roaring by outside the window and a variety of other disturbances. But all of these internal and external events are part of the process of rebirthing. The dog barking can spark off a memory or it can propel the client into anger and irritation at the disruption. This anger then becomes part of the rebirth and, if accepted and followed, it can unveil deeply held belief systems about being ignored for example, or not being important. In this way everything that happens, if accepted without judgement, can lead the rebirthee deeper into himself.

Once again the session mirrors life. In rebirthing nothing is excluded and if this practice is taken into everyday life a whole world of learning opens up to us. Anything, no matter how unpleasant, can take us on an inner journey and, if we are willing to accept what we find there, we discover a wealth of information about ourselves. This is the kind of information that clues us in to what we really want and keeps us in touch with ourselves in the midst of the most stressful and confusing situations.

This, the fifth element of rebirthing, is also important in dealing with expectations. I once had an extremely dramatic client. Each session was full of anguish and tears and strong emotions. This was the way this particular client expressed herself. It is not the way everyone expresses themselves. The sessions were so valuable for her that she recommended two or three friends who also did sessions with me. Unfortunately she had given them a detailed account of what it was like for her. As a result these very different people spent a part of their sessions convinced that rebirthing wasn't working for them or that they were doing something wrong. They came to rebirthing with expectations of what it should be like. When we expect a session to be a certain way we look for signs that it is going according to plan. In other words we accept only what will fit our expectations and exclude everything else. In this way we close our eyes to the opportunities that are right in front of us and come away feeling frustrated and cheated because what *should* have happened, didn't. What happens in a session is unique to each individual and there is no one correct way to do it. There is only your way. Rebirthing is all about surrendering to our own bodies and our breath, about lying back and letting things happen in the unique way they happen for us. One way to prevent things happening is to have rigid expectations or ideas about what should occur, when and how, and then to put lots of effort into making it happen that way. All the rebirthee has to do is relax, accept and breathe and his own unique journey will begin.

Again the session is a microcosm of life. Many of us spend a lot of time and energy trying to do things the way other people do them, trying to look, dress, even talk like other people, because we believe others do it better or correctly. Because of this we under-value or don't even see our own unique talents and way of being. How many times do we tell ourselves 'I couldn't do that job'. Maybe we couldn't do it the way it has always been done but we could do it our way. And how many times do we fail to grasp opportunities because we are so focused on what we expect to happen that we don't see what is actually happening. Rebirthing is an excellent training ground for these invaluable life skills.

The fifth element also applies to the time frame of the material activated. Some people operate entirely in the present. The issues, the belief systems that trouble them, originated in the past but they arise in rebirthing in a present-day context. This means that the rebirthee will be working on difficulties in their current relation-ship, current job, or other areas of their life now. They may glance back occasionally for understanding, because an event from the past comes up in the breathing or because they need to break the ties with someone from their childhood. But the bulk of the work concerns the present. This is perfectly acceptable and it works. Core beliefs, make wrongs, *must*urbations are what need to be resolved and they can be resolved in the here and now. For others the bulk of the work is in the past even though the issues in question are also active in present time. This too works because whatever happens is part of the process.

These are the principal elements of rebirthing but most of the time in rebirthing sessions rebirthees are not thinking along these lines. They are doing and being, rather than analysing. As they become more adept at using the technique, they are able to recog-nise their own patterns of response to what is happening within and are able to remind themselves to apply one or other of the elements. When they realise they are tensing up, for example, they may consciously relax, or they may move towards acceptance of a feeling or sensation once they become aware that they are making that feeling or sensation wrong. Generally they are simply living in the moment.

As I've said earlier, it's impossible to describe what happens in a rebirthing session in words, but let's move in a little closer now and look at the experience as it progresses from the first breath to the fulfilment of completion.

11

The Happening

'The breath is a clear indicator of our inner
life: a bridge between body and mind.'
[David Brazier, *Zen Therapy*]

It is my experience that real, deep and lasting changes take place
through rebirthing. Like Leary and Barron (see chapter 1) nearly
half a century ago, I also believe those changes are made possible
by the fact that rebirthing facilitates non-ordinary states of
consciousness. It is sometimes difficult to explain what such a state
might be like, especially as they can be so fluid and contain many
elements at once. In many rebirthing sessions I have wished for a
recording secretary to take down everything that has transpired
because so many things happen so quickly that I find it difficult to
remember them all afterwards. Of course there is no need to
remember – the issues have been resolved – but remembering
would make it easier to tell others what it is like. One of my
clearest memories of a non-ordinary state comes, not from rebirthing, but from getting mugged late one summer night about three
years ago.

I had parked my car in the driveway of my parents-in-law's
house which is in a less-than-safe part of inner city Dublin. I
walked the rest of the way into the city, had a very pleasant dinner
with friends and walked back to the car with one friend whom I

was going to drive home. As soon as we reached the street where I had parked, I could see that the rear window of the car had been smashed. Because I was so preoccupied with my precious car, I didn't notice that the three men loitering nearby were converging very slowly on us. One of them asked me about the window and told me he could get me a cheap replacement. Being conditioned to respond a certain way to strangers, I thanked him and tried to get out of the conversation without giving offence.

Then suddenly I seemed to enter a different dimension. Time slowed down until it seemed almost to stop moving and I became aware of every logical step of my thought processes. I told myself very calmly that these men were going to attack and began to plan my strategy. With step-by-step precision I worked out that ringing the doorbell of the house would leave us too exposed for too long while whoever was in the house got to the door. The best plan was to wedge myself and my friend between the side of the car and the wrought-iron fence that surrounded the garden. The space was really only wide enough for one person so all three wouldn't be able to go to work at once. All this came in the clearest detail without a trace of panic and it was all worked out in a fraction of a second.

I moved towards my friend who seemed to have been thinking the same way. She backed into the space between the car and the fence and I followed her and the muggers followed me. They were after the bag strapped around my shoulder. I didn't even like the bag and there was very little money in it, but I knew without a shadow of a doubt that they weren't going to get it because suddenly it had become part of me. And they weren't going to violate me. Then I thought 'Here it comes' and suddenly there were hands everywhere, grabbing, hitting. I hunched over the bag and began screaming while my friend threw punches over my head. Then I was hit on the head and my face turned upwards to the sky. It was a beautiful night and the sky was full of stars. I remember thinking how beautiful it was, examining the stars and being aware that there was no moon. Then I became aware of my own voice. Normally I don't have a good scream but my screaming that night was magnificent. Suddenly it expanded to fill the dome of the sky. It was as if, through my voice, I expanded into the sky, filling it, becoming the space between the sky and the ground.

At the same time as I was having this strange experience, I also realised that on a practical level the screaming wasn't working and I had better do something else. So I began kicking. Then just as suddenly as it had begun, the attack stopped and the three men walked away. But, as we were leaning on the car recuperating, one of the men returned. Even in the dim light we could see the indignant rage on his face. He was intending to hurt. At that point something else snapped inside me and I had the most wonderful experience of being totally and utterly fearless. All the conditioning of civilisation and my middle-class upbringing fell away and the freedom was positively heady. I yelled at the man that if he didn't leave us alone I was going to 'kick the fucking shit' out of him and then I made a dive for him. Much to our amusement, he turned and ran away.

Some months later I met another friend who had recently been mugged in the car park of the building where he worked. He too had managed to hold on to his car and his wallet but he had been left frightened and traumatised by the event. Since the incident he has become much more cautious about where he parks and where he walks after dark. I, on the other hand, was energised, empowered, enlivened by the experience. I had tasted a primal freedom, and if anything, I now feel less fearful on the streets at night because of it. The difference, I am positive, was the strange state of consciousness I flipped into while it was happening. It turned a potentially very traumatising experience into an empowering one.

This same alchemy happens in rebirthing sessions. It happens differently for everybody. Sometimes the experience is quite dramatic, sometimes almost psychedelic. Sometimes people

experience memories as they happened and at other times everything is symbolic or surreal. There are times of calm contentment
and there are times when the rebirth is calm, dramatic, realistic,
symbolic and surreal all at once. But, no matter what the
experience, progress through a rebirthing session usually follows
a cycle.

The Energy Cycle

When all five elements of rebirthing are working together, the
process takes the form of energetic cycles that can be experienced
physically, emotionally or mentally or on all three planes at the
same time. One rebirthing session usually contains several such
cycles in which material is activated and resolved. These cycles
are recognised by the rebirthee as a build-up of energy and its
release or as the emergence of a thought pattern, memory or
emotion and its resolution. They are recognised by the rebirther as
changes in the breathing pattern and obvious abreactions (crying,
laughing, trembling, etc.) as well as through the rebirther's own
energetic connection with the client.

The session usually begins with a few minutes of normal breathing. The rebirther may guide the client through the progressive
relaxation of his body and then ask him to focus his attention on
his breathing. This allows the rebirthee time to relax, to ease away
some of the fears he might have, and to begin to be aware of his
breathing. He shouldn't judge anything about his breathing, that it
is too fast or too shallow, for example. The idea is simply to notice
what is happening without judgement.

Gradually, either in his own time or under the guidance of the
rebirther, the rebirthee can begin to deepen and connect his breath,
making it rhythmic and bringing it up into his upper chest. He is
now practising conscious, connected breathing. Soon the body will
take over and maintain this breathing quite naturally for large
portions of the session. The amount of oxygen circulating in the

body rises and the rebirthee soon begins to feel it as the beginning of the energy cycle.

As the diagram below shows, the energy builds up slowly. Some people take several minutes of breathing before they begin to feel any effects, others are aware of physical or emotional reactions straight away. If a rebirthee is already in a highly emotional state before he begins a session then in some respects this first phase is underway before the breathing starts. As the rebirthee continues breathing and accepting everything that is going on for him, the intensity of the energy increases. Eventually it reaches a point of discharge and then there is a lull while the rebirthee is calmly integrating and completing the cycle. One rebirthing session can contain several cycles. The whole process

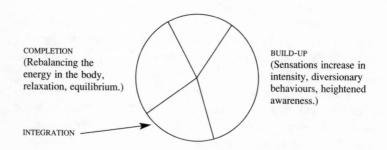

ACTIVATION
(Awareness of physical
sensations. Emotions or
thought patterns begin
to emerge.)

COMPLETION
(Rebalancing the
energy in the body,
relaxation, equilibrium.)

BUILD-UP
(Sensations increase in
intensity, diversionary
behaviours, heightened
awareness.)

INTEGRATION

DISCHARGE
(Nature of energy pattern becomes clear.
Expression of feelings. Dissolution of
energy. All elements working together
leading to integration.)

The Energy Cycle

takes between forty-five minutes and an hour and a quarter but sessions can be shorter or longer than this depending on the individual's natural cycle. The amount of time taken for each stage varies a lot from person to person and session to session. Let's look in greater detail at the different stages and the types of experiences associated with each.

Activation

This can begin slowly or people can become aware of physical or emotional feelings immediately. Some of the physical sensations are light-headedness, tingling in the arms, legs, hands or face, warmth, itching, localised aches, restlessness, pleasure or none of these. Thoughts in this stage can include: 'There's nothing happening'; 'This is a waste of time'; 'What am I doing here?'; 'This is wonderful'; 'I don't want to do this'; 'I can't wait to see what happens next', and so forth. Emotionally, people can be quite calm, excited about the adventure ahead of them, full of fear, angry, rebellious, peaceful ... the whole spectrum of feelings. For some people the fear of facing hidden issues is great and so they begin with gentle breathing, taking as much time in this phase as they need. In fact they may not move beyond this phase for several sessions until they gradually master all of the five elements of rebirthing, realise that they are in total control of the process and that they can trust themselves, and their breath. As their fears subside they are able to progress to the other phases of the cycle. Or they may have been going through the full cycle but on quite a surface level. Now they begin to go deeper into themselves and are able to look at more emotionally charged material.

Build-up

The energy gradually gathers intensity. This can be felt simply as the build-up of tension within the body. All of the sensations of the first phase can be intensified although, at this stage, the

143

rebirthee has usually surrendered to the process to the degree that concerns about its usefulness have disappeared. They are in no doubt that something is happening. Awareness is beginning to expand into areas not normally accessible to our conscious mind. If he hasn't done so already, during build-up the rebirthee can begin to feel strong emotions. He may not be clear about what they are or even that they are emotions, but something is stirring with great intensity that absorbs him on all levels of his being. This is the point where words become inadequate as a means of describing the process.

In the build-up stage diversionary behaviours can come into play. People may yawn, cough, scratch, move, rub their face or head, want to go to the toilet, begin to talk, request a glass of water and so forth. Their physical reactions are a sign that emotions have been stirred up and are manifesting physically. Rebirthees may also go into tetany (see p. 129). There are no hard and fast rules in rebirthing. One person's diversionary behaviour is, for another person, a very valuable expression of what is going on in their internal world. Some people talk a lot during sessions and this is their way of reaching resolution. Others use words to talk themselves out of feelings. An experienced rebirther is usually able to spot the difference. The same is true for dramatic behaviour such as shouting, screaming, thumping the wall or pillows or abject weeping. Some people use laughter as a way of distancing themselves from insights or feelings, others spend an entire session laughing, a belly laugh that comes right from the core of their being, and they go away well satisfied. An odd feature of breathing that may appear during sessions is worth looking at in detail here.

Holding Your Breath
A breath suspension can appear at any point in the cycle but occurs quite often in the build-up phase. This is when the rebirthee holds his breath for short periods of time. It can happen quite a lot with

some clients and it seems to fall into two distinct types. The first is a very sudden stop with the pronounced collapse of the chest as the air is expelled. The rebirthee's breathing is paused until it just as suddenly resumes. The resumption of breathing is usually characterised by a short period of intense distress which the rebirther can help alleviate by telling the client he is safe, instructing him to take a deep breath and by touching his arm or upper chest. The resumption of breathing quickly dissolves the distress. Sometimes these suspensions can have a very deep effect on the whole person and some rebirthers discourage the phenomenon by trying to get the client to continue breathing as soon as they notice the suspension is about to happen. Others believe that it is a natural part of the rebirthing practice and that the rebirthee is processing something that is very difficult for him to deal with in a conscious state.

The other method of holding the breath is less dramatic and quite different from a suspended breath proper. The rebirthee's breath gradually grows shallow. He then stops breathing for one or two breaths at a time. This expands into three, four or more breaths but in between suspensions breathing resumes. This is a very pleasant state for the client and as such is very seductive. It is also very difficult to keep a client alert when this is happening. The techniques used are breathing loudly with the client, talking to them, getting them to sit up, to hold their hand up, asking them to walk around or putting their hand into cold water.

Although this kind of breath suspension is often seen as avoidance behaviour, I have discovered that, in some instances, it can be quite valuable to ask the rebirthee about what is happening for them at the time. Very often they describe a dream-like series of apparently unconnected images, but in the act of describing, the rebirthee often becomes aware that what seems like a bizarre, surreal moving picture actually has great significance. With other rebirthees, talking moves them on through the stage into the emotions that were trying to emerge and the breathing can begin again. For others still, talking has no effect and they continue to hold their breath.

The rebirther can feel this sleepy stage coming before the client's breathing begins to change visibly. In these cases the rebirther feels a drowsiness bordering on drugged sleep and may have to struggle to stay conscious. This is sometimes explained as the release of anaesthetic that has lodged in the client's body from various surgical procedures and even from as long ago as birth. Sometimes rebirthers can even smell the anaesthetic. However, it may also be simply the result of the very strong energetic connection that develops between rebirther and client during a session. Whatever the experience in this stage, sooner or later the build-up reaches a climax and the cycle moves into the discharge phase.

Discharge

This phase is marked by the dissolution of the energy in the body. If the rebirthee's experience is primarily energetic, the discharge may take the form of the energy release described earlier. If the experience is emotional, this is when the emotion reaches its peak. Awareness and acceptance have done their work, the emotion becomes clear and is felt fully. It may be a painful time in the session, the rebirthee may need to express their feelings in tears, sobbing, or occasionally making sounds. Sometimes the climax produces an insight which is not just a mental construct but is felt profoundly in the body and the emotions. This is a multi-dimensional experience that takes place in a non-ordinary state of consciousness, and an insight that comes in this manner can have a lasting effect on the rebirthee's behaviour and thought patterns.

The energy can also climax in a memory, often a memory of birth. Again these are multi-dimensional and not just the visual phenomenon tinged with feeling that we usually call memory. If they are very old memories, they may not be very visual at all. Instead they are whole body experiences, sense memories which can be far more real than the memories we can recall at will every day. Memories in rebirthing are an interesting phenomenon. When they occur they can seem very real, three-dimensional events. Yet there is another part of the rebirthee that is fully aware of where they are and what they are doing. The first time I revisited my birth I was fully aware that I was lying on a mattress in my rebirther's front room with my hands by my side and my body supported steadily by the floor. Yet at the same time I felt my right arm stretched above my head, there was an intense pain radiating from my heart down my left arm and my body seemed to be rocking as if it were lying on waves in an ocean. It took me some minutes to realise what was happening and that at that point I seemed to have two bodies, one which was being born in a very real way and one which was standing back very sensibly watching the proceedings.

For others, the journey is symbolic. I have had many clients who have visions of themselves on clifftops, climbing through dark and frightening rock formations or floating alone in the middle of desolate waters which, as they breathe, turn into mountain tops, summer meadows, or warm caves. These images are not just visual. They also have emotional, cognitive and even spiritual dimensions, but it is the visual aspect that is most open to description. Stanislav Grof, in his book *The Holotropic Mind*, links particular symbolic visions to the different stages of birth.[38] My clients have generally not analysed them in such depth but have been content to know that through their symbolic experiences, they themselves have changed.

Other rebirthees see people who speak to them. I personally have never had such an experience so I can't interpret what it might mean. As a rebirther I consider it part of my job to keep my own interpretations, belief systems or scepticism out of my clients' sessions. They interpret their own experience and they have explained these companions of their inner world as archetypal figures, personifications of aspects of their own psyche, as spirit guides or as entities they had been aware of during their childhood but with whom they had lost contact as they grew into adolescence.

In every case they have described the encounters as deeply rewarding.

Whatever way the rebirthee's session plays out, the purpose of the whole exercise is integration and integration generally happens somewhere towards the end of the discharge stage and before completion begins.

Integration

It is the point of integration where issues are truly and lastingly resolved. Colin Sissons says 'The process of integration is permitting ourselves to become fully aware of something we once avoided through suppression and now choose to enjoy it.'[39] Whatever about enjoying it in the conventional sense of the word, we choose to experience it fully without judgement. And when we do it loses its grip on us. It is integrated into the fabric of our selves and our lives so that it no longer exercises an inordinate influence on us. The way we feel, the way we behave, the unspoken messages we put out to others change in a real and lasting way.

Again integration is a multi-dimensional experience. For those who experience it physically it can feel like a weight being lifted off the body. Energetically it is the dissipation of the intense energy that has built up in the body. It can be marked by the simple fading away of even the most intense emotion or it can be a full body knowingness that something has changed profoundly. Integration moves the rebirthee into the final phase, completion.

Completion

After integration there is a resting phase during which the cycle completes itself. Between cycles, completion is a period of calm and well-being before the next cycle begins but the completion at the end of a session is particularly important and can take some time. This is the period when everything that has happened is consolidated and the body, mind and emotions settle down and readjust to the changes that have taken place. Completion is often characterised by very deep physical relaxation, a profound sense of peacefulness, lightness, clarity, contentment and sometimes euphoria.

It is very important to complete a session adequately and clients learn very quickly when they have reached that stage. But sometimes, for various reasons, they don't give themselves enough time. An experienced rebirther can usually spot this and ask their client to breathe gently for a few more minutes. They may still insist that they are complete but find out very quickly when they try to stand up that they are dizzy or that their body is still vibrating. Even if no physical symptoms are present and the client is grounded and clear headed enough to drive home, they may not be complete emotionally. In this case they may feel quite 'raw' the next day or may suffer the unresolved residue of what was going on for them in the session. The situation is easily rectified by ten minutes or so of breathing but it is much better to do this during the session rather than several days later without the support of the rebirther. The length of the completion phase varies greatly and sometimes rebirthees like to be left alone to listen to some music. Completion is vitally important and shouldn't be rushed.

When the rebirthee has reached equilibrium and feels ready to move back into the world, he and the rebirther can end the session.

Ending the Session

After completion, some people want to talk about what happened in the session. This can be helpful in consolidating gains made. Other have reached a point of such complete resolution that to talk about what went on is like covering old ground that is no longer very interesting or important. Most will give the rebirther a brief run down on what happened during the breathing and together they may discuss work to be done between sessions. Sometimes, at this juncture, a cup of tea and some chocolate biscuits are very welcome. In fact, I would go so far as to say that if you haven't tasted chocolate biscuits after a rebirthing session, then you have never really tasted chocolate biscuits.

What I have just attempted to describe is a rebirthing session done with a trained rebirther. But there are other aspects to rebirthing besides the psychotherapeutic one we have been discussing so far. In the next chapter we will look at using the technique to rebirth yourself, but we'll also look at how to use rebirthing for stress management and the enhancement of creativity and creative living.

12

☯

Rebirthing at Home

Manage stress, win the Booker prize and save the world . . .

Sooner or later most people who take sessions with a rebirther begin to rebirth themselves at home. I have found that some clients may begin rebirthing themselves after just one session but that is rare. Most people need longer than that to become skilled at using the technique effectively by themselves. Often they begin with just five or ten minutes of conscious connected breathing and build up from that into a full self-rebirth.

When people use rebirthing at home they usually lie down in the same way that they would with a rebirther and breathe in exactly the same way as they do in sessions. If you are currently taking rebirthing sessions and haven't talked to your rebirther about self-rebirthing, I suggest that you bring up the subject the next time you meet them. If you've never taken sessions with a rebirther, I don't recommend you try self-rebirthing. But for those of you who already know how to use the rebirthing technique and want to start rebirthing yourselves, you can ease into the practice by beginning with short periods of conscious connected breathing.

Find a comfortable chair in a place where you won't be disturbed and relax for a few minutes. Then become aware of your breathing and the feelings associated with it. Use your breath to quieten your mind and bring your attention inward. Then gently and slowly begin to bring your breath up into your chest. At this point your goal is to simply observe the breath and the feelings and sensations you experience with every inhale and exhale. Don't breathe too fast or too fully, just enough to enjoy yourself. After five minutes or so, ease down your breathing until it is back to normal and you are ready to return to your daily activities. With practice you can increase the time spent breathing until you feel ready to lie down and give yourself a full rebirthing session. The experience is quite different from that of a supervised rebirth, but it is still very valuable. Some of my clients have also told me that a few gentle connected breaths are excellent for quietening a racing mind at bedtime and has them nodding off within minutes.

For people who have never taken a rebirthing session, but want a flavour of what rebirthing is like, try the twenty connected breaths exercise at the end of this chapter. This is a good exercise to boost flagging energy. In a tense or difficult encounter or meeting I find it's very good for 'clearing the air', almost like an air freshener. It works best if you can get everyone involved to do it together, but you can also do it very effectively by yourself. If you have a specific task to concentrate on, twenty connected breaths can be used to clear your mind before you begin.

Managing stress

So far we have been looking at rebirthing largely in the context of dealing with old, unresolved issues from the past. I find that it also has a very valuable role to play in other areas of life, particularly in the management of stress.

The word stress as it is currently used seems to have two broad meanings. The first is as a description of the host of pressures and demands that people find themselves trying to cope with on a daily basis. These are external stressors. The same word is also used to describe the particular set of physical responses people have to those external pressures. This reaction to external pressures is known as the 'stress response' and is produced by what is called the sympathetic branch of the nervous system. When the stress response is triggered, the whole body is put on alert. Digestion stops, blood flow increases, blood pressure rises as does the level of clotting agent in the blood and the liver releases sugar for energy. Muscles grow tense, the senses become more alert and breathing moves into the chest as the abdominal muscles contract to protect the internal organs. We are ready for action. When exam time comes around, or we have to give a speech, make a presentation or respond quickly in an emergency, the stress response is invaluable. It sharpens our senses, focuses our thinking and gives us the energy to accomplish things we couldn't do under normal circumstances.

When the situation that triggered the stress response is resolved, the parasympathetic branch of the nervous system restores the body to normal functioning. But what if the response doesn't abate? What if we are under constant stress and a low level of the stress response is activated in our body for long periods? A wide range of symptoms and illnesses have been related to stress. The most familiar are heart attacks, angina, headaches, back pain and fatigue. But less severe signs that people are under stress are irritability, forgetfulness, muddled thinking, difficulty making decisions, excessive talking, laughing at the wrong moment, frequent colds and flu, constipation, diarrhoea, difficulty sleeping and a range of other symptoms.

A Stress-management Plan

It's very important to become aware of stress levels and to do something about them before they translate into serious physical problems. For many people, this can be a relatively simple matter of rearranging schedules and delegating tasks, but for others a more comprehensive stress-management plan is needed. Some of the basic elements of such a plan include:

- awareness;
- time and life management;
- self-esteem;
- assertiveness;
- nutrition and exercise;
- relaxation techniques.

The most basic element of stress management is *awareness*. Many people rush through their day never really tuning in to themselves or their bodies. The only time they take for themselves is when they realise that they have a splitting headache or their back hurts and they have to stop and take a pill to ease the pain. A simple way to increase your awareness is to slowly and consciously relax every section of your body beginning with your head and working down to your toes. This will help you become aware of your stress levels and exactly where in your body you are holding the stress. The skill of awareness practised in rebirthing is an even better method of recognising stress on an ongoing basis.

Once you're aware that you are feeling the effects of stress, you can begin to do something about it. Some things can be done immediately and with relatively little effort. You can move and exercise the parts of your body that are stiff, go for a walk or make small changes in your diet. You can take some time out to do things which relax you and let you switch off your mind for a while. If your stress is caused by having too much to do every day, then you might begin to work out ways of using your time more effectively. Time management can include delegating tasks to other people. If you do this you need to be prepared to accept the way they do the job. Your spouse or partner may not be as particular as you are about ironing the clothes or arranging socks in the drawer according to colour, size and texture. Time management also includes working out systems that make life easier. If you have no filing system for bills and other documents, for example, you might find yourself wasting a lot of time rooting through the same box full of papers several times a month, usually in a desperate hurry because you've left it to the last minute. A little accordion file would cut out a lot of frustration and save a lot of time. Making a list of all the things you have to do in a day or a week and prioritising them is also useful. Make sure time for yourself is near the top of the list. Then cut out the stuff that's not necessary or enjoyable.

Stress and Self-esteem

Stress doesn't affect everybody equally. Some people thrive under pressure, while others are destroyed by it. One of the reasons for this difference is that people vary widely in how they cope with stress. Many things contribute to a person's ability to cope but one of the most important is their level of *self-esteem*. And this is one of the areas of stress management where rebirthing can help the most.

There are many definitions of the term self-esteem and most people's self-esteem is lower in some situations than in others. Basically a person with high self-esteem is confident, believes in themselves and pursues what they want in life without worrying unduly about what other people will think of them. Fundamental to a high level of self-esteem are strong, life-enhancing core beliefs. These are the same core beliefs we discussed in chapter 4. A person with strong limiting core beliefs about himself and life, a person with low self-esteem in other words, is more likely to buckle under stress than a person whose strong sense of self-worth empowers them to act assertively in difficult situations. Poor copers also experience stress in a wider range of situations. A high self-esteem person might get nervous at the idea of speaking before an audience but they could go through with it and might even enjoy themselves. On the other hand, the person who is still labouring under the weight of unresolved issues from the past can find even a trip to the supermarket stressful.

Rebirthing and Stress Management

Rebirthing tackles the problem of stress on two levels. The internal causes of stress – our core belief systems and attitudes – are changed in a fundamental and lasting way through the psycho-therapeutic aspects of rebirthing. This means that rebirthing is a powerful technique for the long-term management of stress. It often comes as quite a surprise to many rebirthees when they discover that they can cope easily with situations that previously would have devastated them. This includes one-off events like going to a party, giving a speech or standing up for themselves with people in authority. It also applies to circumstances they have to face every day such as unmanageable children or a bad relationship – the kind of grinding stress that can lead to illness.

But rebirthing is also an invaluable tool in immediate moments of crisis. One of the body's first responses to stress is to alter the breathing patterns, sometimes shutting down the whole breathing mechanism for moments at a time or by hyperventilating. Rapid, shallow, mid-chest breathing is part of the stress response, and as we've already seen in chapter 2, this particular breathing pattern itself causes stress in the body. The effect varies. Some people are paralysed into inaction, others think quite clearly, and still others have nervous reactions like giggling or panic. Almost always people lose contact with what they are feeling. This means that the feelings are not processed or integrated and are stored in the body in the same way as unresolved issues from that past are. Being detached from our feelings also means that they are not at our disposal to inform our actions. In times of stress, our tendency is to flip over into the largely cerebral activity of controlling the situation as much as possible and finding a way of restoring the status quo. This is not solving the problem. It's simply trying to get things back to the way they were.

Maintaining deep, connected breaths right in the moment of stress can reconnect people with their feelings and, at the same time, allow them to manage those feelings rather than be overwhelmed by them. Being connected to our feelings and managing them means that we are not panicked into over control. It also means we can use those feelings as at least partial guides to how we need to react in the situation. Being calmly in touch with ourselves means that we are more likely to know what we really want and where we really stand in a difficult situation. We can let events proceed around us, playing a part in the action that is true to ourselves. In this way we are less likely to waste time afterwards obsessing about what we should have done, what we should have said or regretting missed opportunities.

Breathwork is vital to stress management and is a fundamental element of most relaxation techniques. The deep relaxation brought about by rebirthing makes it a very powerful way to rejuvenate the body and mind and many rebirthees report increased levels of energy and aliveness. This comes not just from the physiological effects of more efficient breathing, but also from the psychotherapeutic effects of the technique. As old issues are integrated, the energy previously involved in keeping feelings at bay is now free to be used in more life-enhancing ways. And because rebirthing works with both the long- and short-term causes of stress, it is one of the most powerful stress-management techniques available.

Creativity

Another way of working with rebirthing at home is by using it to enhance the whole area of creativity and creative living. When people think of the word 'creativity', they usually think of artists, writers and musicians producing original works of art, creating something new that has never been done before. But there is truth in the old folk-wisdom 'There's nothing new under the sun'. Think of the novels you've read recently. Now strip away the personalities of the characters, the circumstances and setting of their lives. How many truly different plots are left?

All creativity is based on what came before and most artists, musicians and writers readily acknowledge their influences. Creativity is about seeing possibilities and connections that haven't yet been seen. It's about putting existing elements together in ways nobody else has thought of. Because those elements have never been together in quite that manner before, something new is produced with properties and qualities that are also new. In time, someone else will take this new creation and use it as an element in their own creative work.

This process of creativity is not confined to the world of art. Scientists are often exceptionally creative people, seeing possibilities where none apparently existed before. So are computer and software designers, architects and teachers. Everybody has the capacity to be creative. In the course of my work I have seen the most stunning works of art produced by community groups and retirement clubs. But everything, even the most mundane daily tasks, can be creative. The dynamic of creativity, seeing connections and possibilities, is the same for the artist as it is for the person sitting at home trying to work out how to remove a rusted nut from a bicycle or a quicker way to do the ironing.

An Uncluttered Mind

There are many ways, both long- and short-term, in which rebirthing can contribute to creativity. In my experience it does this by nurturing the conditions in which the creative act thrives. One of the most basic of these conditions is an uncluttered mind. Stories are legion of scientists and thinkers who found it so difficult to solve problems that had arisen in their work that they simply gave up. Later, after sleep or while relaxing and generally not thinking very much at all, the solution came unbidden to their mind. An uncluttered mind fosters the ability to make connections and put elements together in novel ways. Many of the thoughts, worries and concerns that crowd the mind are the product of unresolved issues and limiting core beliefs. Resolving these issues, trans-

158

forming core beliefs, is an obvious way in which rebirthing can have a long-term effect in the area of creativity.

Expanding Awareness

If novel ideas and solutions come to people while they are sleeping or relaxing, then in these cases the creative process is taking place unconsciously, outside the range of day-to-day awareness. Non-ordinary states of consciousness are times of greatly expanded awareness when the concept of time as well as many of the normal mental constructs have dissolved. But using conscious connected breathing more casually and for shorter periods can have a less dramatic yet similar effect.

The method I use and which several of my clients have discovered for themselves, is to lie down comfortably for ten or fifteen minutes. Begin breathing consciously and connect the inhale and exhale. Breathing should be rhythmic but not unusually deep or fast. There must be no effort or strain of any kind, just a natural, comfortable rhythm. Then bring to mind whatever it is you want to focus on. This could be the plot of a story you are writing, a mechanical problem with the car, a relationship difficulty . . . anything. Bring it to mind and let it hover there. It is very important not to put any effort into thinking about it. Just hold it in your awareness and breathe gently. It is my experience that solutions come effortlessly. As so little scientific research into rebirthing has yet been done, there is no immediate answer as to why this can happen. Russian research into the effects of what the Russians call 'free breathing' remain untranslated. However, they do indicate that conscious breathing affects the bioelectric activity of the brain as well as increasing the activity of the parasympathetic nervous system.[40]

Creative Living

Solving problems, developing the plot of a play or the melodic line of a piece of music form the detail of creative activity. But the creative act in the wider context is the product of reaching deep inside oneself and examining what is there. People who don't know who they are will find this a very difficult thing to do. The person who has lost sight of their own interests, needs and desires because they have spent their lives trying to please others, can spend many years chasing other people's dreams. They may pursue careers, relationships and modes of self-expression because that's what they think is expected of them, what they *should* do. Creative living, when our lives are an expression of who we are rather than who we think we should be, is fostered through rebirthing and emerges as the layers of our conditioning are peeled away.

Affirmations

Another technique many rebirthers recommend is auto-suggestion or affirmations. Carefully chosen affirmations support the work done in rebirthing sessions but auto-suggestion is also a very useful and popular personal development technique that can be used at home.

Affirmations are positive statements carefully designed to counter the negative messages we feed ourselves every day. If we kept a diary of our thoughts we might find that a disproportionately large number of them are devoted to criticism and pessimism. Listening to a daily stream of limiting beliefs and attitudes takes a toll on our lives. Our thoughts affect our behaviour, our tone of voice and our body language and, as such, have a direct bearing upon how other people react to us. If you find this hard to believe try the mind and body exercise at the end of this chapter. This is a modified version of an exercise used in the bodywork system called Body Harmony. I use it in almost every group I run and it never fails to produce dramatic results. Whether they are aware of it or not, people respond to our thoughts and attitudes as they are given expression in our methods of communication.

The technique of affirmation is generally credited to Louise Hay, but it probably originated in the early 1900s with French pharmacist Emile Coué. Coué discovered the power of auto-suggestion and developed the laws of suggestion. His famous affirmation was 'Every day in every way I'm getting better and better'. Since then the practice has been developed and refined for use by almost everyone in every situation. In developing affirmations for personal use the following guidelines can be useful.

Write Simple Affirmations

Affirmations are simple statements, the shorter the better. Very long, convoluted affirmations obscure the message we are trying to get across and confuse the mind. Laziness also works against us when we try to make ourselves write long affirmations.

> Example: *I, John, accept my body as it is now.*
> is better than: *I, John, now accept the divine creation that is my body, which supports and nurtures me and has served me well in life.*

Structure and Tense

Affirmations are written in the present tense using your name where possible. This tells your mind that the suggestion you are feeding it is a done deed, it is already a reality. As adults our negative thoughts are ours, but that wasn't necessarily always the case. We encountered many of those beliefs for the first time in what other people said to us (in both words and actions) and in what they said about us. To counter all these influences, affirmations can also be written in first, second and third person singular.

> Example: *The world supports me, Jane, in everything I do.*
> *The world supports you, Jane, in everything you do.*
> *The world supports Jane in everything she does.*

Know Your Thoughts

Affirmations help reprogram our minds. But this is just one of their functions. They are also diagnostic tools, one of the means by which we uncover deeper and deeper layers of our thinking. The first step in developing an affirmation is to get to know exactly what it is you want to change in your thinking. Get as close as possible to the root thought or belief. You can assist yourself in doing this by writing down what it is that you want and turn it into a starter affirmation. Then, as you write the affirmation, you also write your response to it. This can be an emotional response such as anger or fear, a physical response such as throwing the pen across the room, or a verbal response. Whatever it is, pick up the pen again and write it down. You can do this on one side of the page or keep a separate page for the responses. When you have filled a page or two, go back over your responses. Is there a thought there that goes deeper, has a greater charge for you than the affirmation you are writing? If there is, then this may be a deeper-level affirmation for you to work on. If not, then you are probably on the right track with your original affirmation. (You may not need to fill a page or two before this more bottom-line thought pops out at you.)

Example:	*I want a good, supportive relationship.*
Becomes the affirmation:	*I, Tom, now have a good, supportive relationship.*

AFFIRMATION	RESPONSE
I, Tom, now have a good, supportive relationship.	*No I don't this is rubbish.*
I, Tom, now have a good, supportive relationship.	*Sadness and feelings of regret.*
I, Tom, now have a good, supportive relationship.	*How could I, women/men don't like me.*

162

I, Tom, now have a good, supportive relationship.	*Anger, slash page with pen.*
I, Tom, now have a good, supportive relationship.	*I'm too repulsive for people to like me.*
I, Tom, now have a good, supportive relationship.	*Feelings of revulsion.*

At this stage it has become apparent to Tom that his belief that he is repulsive to men/women carries a stronger emotional punch than the affirmation he is doing. His ultimate goal is to remove his internal obstacles to forming a good relationship, but telling himself that he has one already is pretty useless when strong feelings of self-revulsion are hidden underneath. Alternative affirmations he could use that would reach closer to his bottom-line thoughts are:

I, Tom, accept myself as I am now.
I, Tom, am an attractive, loveable man.
I, Tom, am clean and innocent the way I am now.

In writing affirmations it is very important to choose the words carefully so they will have meaning and power for you.

Ways of Using Affirmations

Affirmations are traditionally written about thirty times a day for three to four weeks or until the negative responses fade away. But they can also be spoken. They can be said while looking in a mirror, sung, shouted or put on tape and played throughout the day. Taped affirmations are particularly good for playing as one falls asleep. It is also good to do affirmations in conjunction with exercise. The movement of the body seems to enhance the message being programmed into the mind and this method also has the advantage of allowing us to time the affirmation to the rhythm of

163

deep breathing. Another particularly effective way of doing affirmations is to sit comfortably and begin conscious connected
breathing. Then say the first word of the affirmation with an
inbreath allowing that word to sink down into the body with the
breath. Then exhale and say the second word with the next inhale
and so forth. For more information on using affirmations or auto-
suggestion, consult Louise Hay's book, *You Can Heal Your Life*
or *The Wizard Within* by A M Krasner (see Selected Reading).

The following breathing exercises can be done at home. The
twenty connected breaths is a classic rebirthing taster exercise
while the breath awareness is a gentle technique that can function
as a meditation to aid relaxation. The final two exercises should
help you compose suitable affirmations you can use every day.

Exercises

1 Breath Awareness

Sit comfortably in a quiet room where you won't be
interrupted. Close your eyes and become aware of your
breathing. Breathing through your nose, spend some time
noticing the sensations in the space between your upper lip and
your nose. Now move your attention into your nostrils and keep
your attention there, exploring the sensation of air in your nose.
Follow the breath into your throat. Notice the temperature, the
feel of it in your throat. Then move down into your lungs. Feel
them slowly filling up. Pay attention to the detail of
temperature, sensation, expansion, what it feels like for your
lungs to be full. When you feel full try taking in even more air.
What does that feel like? Notice the sensations at the top of
your breath, in the second between fullness and exhale. Then
exhale and pay attention to how that feels. What does it feel
like to have empty lungs?
Repeat this sequence several times slowly and then, as you go
through it again, focus your attention on just one point – in
your nose, throat or in your lungs. Keep your attention on that
point and continue breathing slowly for at least five minutes.

When you feel comfortable with this exercise, you can increase the amount of time you spend on it and use it as a daily meditation.

2 Twenty Connected-Breaths

Sit comfortably with your eyes closed. Take note of how you feel physically, mentally and emotionally. Are you feeling light, heavy, frustrated, calm, angry, peaceful, etc? Are there aches or pains anywhere in your body? Is your mind racing, languishing, or something in between? Look around the room. Note the textures, colours, the brightness or dimness of everything.

Now become aware of your breathing. You can breathe through either your nose or your mouth. Either way, notice the air going in and going out. Is it fast or slow, deep or shallow, flowing or halting? How it is doesn't matter, just notice it. Then become aware of any pauses between breaths and begin connecting inhale and exhale. When you have done this, begin breathing more fully and bring the breath into your upper chest. Take it easy, you are not in a competition so be gentle with yourself. Take four full, connected breaths into your upper chest. Make the fifth breath even fuller, as if it is coming right up over your head. Then take four more full, connected breaths into your upper chest followed by a fifth breath over your head. Repeat this cycle twice more until you have taken twenty connected rebirthing breaths.

Now notice your feelings. Are there new feelings? Have the old ones changed in any way? How are your aches and pains? Have they intensified, gone away, changed in any way? If you have breathed very vigorously, you may feel a little light-headed. This is okay and will pass. Look around the room. Has there been any change in your visual perception? Do you consider the experience pleasant, unpleasant or are you feeling quite neutral about it? No matter what you feel, don't make it wrong. The breath is simply bringing out what is already there.

3 Mind and Body

For this you need at least one and preferably several friends. Find one of your negative thoughts or beliefs about yourself. Then turn it into an affirmation. Stand in front of your friends and ask them to observe your body language very carefully. Tell them you are going to be thinking about something and then you are going to think the opposite and you want them to tell you if they can spot the point when you change your mind. Begin saying the negative belief to yourself several times. Then, when you are ready start saying your affirmation to yourself repeatedly. Do not try to control your body during this exercise. Concentrate solely on the messages you are feeding yourself. Your friends will be able to tell you when you have changed your mind. Ask them to be specific about how they knew when the change took place. People are reading our thoughts through our body every day and we are reading theirs.

4 Create an Affirmation
Pick a situation which you would like to change. What exactly would you like to change? What is the ideal outcome for you? Then close your eyes and imagine the situation. Run it through in your mind. Note your feelings and write them down. Do the same with what you are thinking. Then go over the thoughts, saying them to yourself until you find the one that has the strongest physical or energetic charge for you. Remember you cannot change the way other people behave or think so concentrate on your own thoughts in that situation. Turn that thought into an affirmation and begin working with it. Use a response column (see p.162) and if one of the responses demands to be turned into an affirmation do so. Work with it until you have no more negative responses and see if anything changes in the situation. If all that changes is the way you feel, then the affirmation has done its work.

13

@

Journey's End

We have examined rebirthing as a tool of psychotherapy, as a means of managing stress and as a method of enhancing creativity. Rebirthing is an experiential breathing technique that can be used with almost any psychotherapeutic system or programme of deep personal development. It can also fit in with almost anyone's religious beliefs, including no religious belief at all. Rebirthing is not connected to any church, religion or religious practice but many people, as they proceed through a series of rebirthing sessions, have what they describe as spiritual experiences. I find that after eight or nine sessions many clients begin to explore spiritual matters.

This is a natural development from a process that facilitates psychological growth through the transpersonal experiences of non-ordinary states of consciousness. In other words, as rebirthees get in touch with the self that lies beneath their conditioning, the technique leads to a state of being similar to what seminar and workshop leader Anthony de Mello calls 'waking up' and an approximation of what psychotherapist David Brazier calls 'Buddha Nature'[41]. It is being at the fulcrum of existence, at the still centre of the storm where happiness does not depend on the absence of suffering, on circumstances, on achievement or on being good. There is a sense of place in something that is greater than the self. It is greater in that it is more than the individual, yet this something *is* each individual. Each person is all of creation and all of creation is in each person. It is a blissful state of being fully present in the moment, needing nothing and connected to everything.

Some people define this experience in terms of Jesus. Others speak of a higher consciousness or a Great Spirit. Still more describe it as being at one with the ecosystem, all things, consciousness. This calm surety of connection to creation is a profoundly enlivening experience and serves the very human psychological need for a sense of place in the world, regardless of who we are and what we do. The journey inwards becomes a journey outwards. And for those interested in exploring their inner world further, the rebirthing organisations listed in the appendices should be able to help you find a rebirther in your area.

Enjoy your journey!

APPENDICES

❦

Notes

1 Yalom, Irvin, *The Theory and Practice of Group Psychotherapy*, Basic Books Inc., NY, 1975
2 Stevens, Jay, *Storming Heaven, LSD and the American Dream*. Paladin Books, UK, 1989, p. 46
3 Stevens, Jay, *ibid*, p. 103
4 Orr, Leonard, quoted in Gunnel Minett's *Breath and Spirit*: *Rebirthing as a Healing Tool*, Aquarian Press, UK, 1994
5 Patel, Dr Chandra, *The Complete Guide to Stress Management*, Macdonald Optima, UK, 1989
6 Manne, Joy, Ph.D., 'Breath is a Language', paper presented to the Fourth Global Inspiration Conference of the International Breathwork Foundation, Austria, 1997
7 Fried, Robert, *Breathe Well, Be Well*, John Wiley & Sons Inc., CA 1999, p. 130
8 For more information on using breathing to control stammering, write to McGuire Programme Ireland, PO Box 119, Cork, Ireland
9 Rosenberg, Jack, *Body, Self and Soul: Sustaining Integration*, Humanics Ltd, US, 1991, p. 20

10 Verny, Dr Thomas with Kelly, John, *The Secret Life of the Unborn Child*, Warner Books, US, 1996, p. 152

11 Morningstar, Jim, 'Breathwork – Therapy of Choice for Whom?', *The Healing Breath: A Journal of Breathwork Practice, Psychology and Spirituality*, Vol. 1, 1999, website: http://www.i-breathe.com

12 Chamberlain, Dr David, *The Mind of Your Newborn Baby*, North Atlantic Books, CA, 1998, pp. 11–13

13 Dr Robert Fried in his book *Breathe Well, Be Well* shows that the music most conducive to relaxation (including baroque) has melodic phrases that are approximately the same length as the inspiration phase of the average human breath. *Op. cit.* p. 185

14 Verny, Dr Thomas with Kelly, John, *The Secret Life of the Unborn Child*, Warner Books, UK, 1996, pp. 6–7

15 Mauger, Benig, *Songs From the Womb: Healing the Wounded Mother*, Collins Press, Ireland, 1998, pp. 15–49

16 Mauger, *ibid*, p. 54

17 Verny, *ibid*, p. 85

18 Verny, *ibid*, pp. 93–94

19 Ray, Sondra and Mandel, Bob, *Birth and Relationships: How Your Birth Affects Your Relationships*, Celestial Arts, CA, 1987

20 Mauger *ibid*, p. 102

21 Begg, *ibid*, p. 103

22 Mauger, *ibid*, p. 103

23 Ray and Mandel, *ibid*, p. 99–101

24 Verny, *ibid*, p. 108

25 Ray and Mandel, *ibid*, p. 105

26 Begg, *ibid*, p. 102

27 Verny, *ibid*, p. 89

28 Erikson, Erik, *Childhood and Society*, Penguin Books, UK, 1965

29 Verny, *ibid*, p. 131

30 For a very practical guide to child-centred parenting see, Dyer, Wayne, *What Do Your Really Want for Your Children?*, Avon Books, NY, 1985

31 See Beatie, Melody, *Codependent No More*, Hazelden, US, 1987

32 See Saunders, Alex *et al*, *It Hurts Me Too: Children's Experiences of Domestic Violence and Refuge Life*, Saunders, WAFF, NISW, ChildLine, UK, 1995

33 Chamberlain, *op cit*, p. 218

34 For a comprehensive review of the patterns of relationship see Humphreys, Tony, *Myself, My Partner*, Gill & Macmillan, Ireland, 1998

35 Hoeg, Peter, *Miss Smilla's Feeling for Snow*, Harvill Press, UK, 1993

36 Taylor, Kylea and Manne, Joy, 'Dialogue on Hyperventilation', *The Healing Breath*, Vol. 1, 1999

37 Minett, *ibid*, p. 65

38 Grof, Stanislav, *The Holotropic Mind*, Harper, CA, 1993, pp. 33–82

39 Sissons, Colin, *Rebirthing Made Easy*, Total Press, New Zealand, 1990, p. 6

40 *Breath and Inspiration*, IBF Newsletter, July-August, 1999

41 See de Mello, Anthony, *Awareness*, Fount Paperbacks, UK, 1990 and Brazier, David, *Zen Therapy*, Constable & Co Ltd, UK, 1995

❧ Selected Reading

Rebirthing/Breathwork Books

Begg, Deike, *Rebirthing: Freedom from Your Past*, Thorsons, UK, 1999

Fried, Robert, Ph.D., *Breathe Well, Be Well*, John Wiley & Sons, Inc. NY, 1999

Hendricks, Gay, *Conscious Breathing: Breathwork for Health, Stress Release and Personal Mastery*, Bantam Books, NY, 1995

Leonard, Jim and Laut, Phil *Rebirthing: The Science of Enjoying All of Your Life*, Trinity Publications, CA, 1983

Manne, Joy *Soul Therapy*, North Atlantic Books, CA, 1997

Minett, Gunnel, *Breath and Spirit: Rebirthing as a Healing Tool*, Aquarian Press, UK, 1994

Orr, Leonard, and Ray, Sondra *Rebirthing in the New Age*, Celestial Arts, CA, 1983

Ray, Sondra *Celebration of Breath*, Celestial Arts, CA, 1983

Sissons, Colin, *Rebirthing Made Easy*, Total Press, New Zealand, 1985

Swami Ambikananda Saraswati, *Principles of Breathwork*, Thorsons, UK, 1999

Taylor, Kylea, *The Breathwork Experience: Exploration and Healing in Non-ordinary States of Consciousness*, Hanford Mead, CA, 1994

Rebirthing/Breathwork Articles

Breathe: The International Breathwork Magazine, editor Robert Moore, 7 Silver Street, Buckfastleigh, Devon TQ11 0BQ, UK

The Healing Breath: A Journal of Breathwork Practice, Psychology and Spirituality, editor Joy Manne, website: http://www.i-breathe.com./

Ehrmann, Wilfried, 'Breath is Your Companion', paper presented at the Fourth Global Inspiration Conference of the International Breathwork Foundation, 1997

Gorsky, Sergei, 'Breathwork – Instant Charm and Hidden Dangers', paper presented at the Fourth Global Inspiration Conference of the International Breathwork Foundation, 1997

Manne, Joy 'Breath is a Language', paper presented at the Fourth Global Inspiration Conference of the International Breathwork Foundation, 1997

Manne, Joy, 'Rebirthing, an Orphan Therapy or a Member of the Family of Psychotherapies?' *International Journal of Prenatal and Perinatal Psychology and Medicine*, 1994, Vol. 6, No. 4, pp. 503–517.

Morningstar, Jim, 'Breathwork – Therapy of Choice for Whom?', *The Healing Breath: A Journal of Breathwork Practice, Psychology and Spirituality*, 1997, editor Joy Manne, website: http://www.i-breathe.com

Taylor, Kylea, 'Yogic Sleep and Meditation States During Holotropic Breathwork' in *Newsletter*, June 1998, International Breathwork Foundation

Note: *You can access most of these articles either through the internet journal* The Healing Breath *(www.i-breathe.com) or from the International Breathwork Foundation.*

General

Adler, Alfred, editor Brett, Colin, *Social Interest, Adler's Key to the Meaning of Life*, Oneworld, UK, 1998

Beatie, Melody, *Codependent No More*, Hazelden, US, 1987

Brazier, David, *Zen Therapy*, Constable & Co Ltd UK, 1995

Chamberlain, Dr David, *The Mind of Your Newborn Baby*, North Atlantic Books, CA, 1998

de Mello, Anthony, *Awareness*, Fount Paperbacks, UK, 1990

Dyer, Dr Wayne, *What Do You Really Want for Your Children?*, Avon Books, NY, 1985

Ellis, Albert, *Humanistic Psychotherapy*, Julian Press and McGraw-Hill, NY, 1973.

Erikson, Erik, *Childhood and Society*, Penguin Books, UK, 1965

Frankel, Victor, *Man's Search for Meaning*, Washington Square Press, NY, 1959

Goleman, Daniel, *Emotional Intelligence: Why It Can Matter More Than IQ*, Bloomsbury, UK, 1996

Hay, Louise, *You Can Heal Your Life*, Eden Grove, UK, 1988

Humphreys, Dr Tony *Myself, My Partner*, Gill & Macmillan, Ireland, 1998

Jung, CJ, *Memories, Dreams, Reflections* (ed. Jaffe, A.) London, Fontana, 1995.

Krasner, AM *The Wizard Within*, American Board of Hypnotherapy, US, 1990

Leboyer, Frederick, *Birth Without Violence*, Mandarin, UK, 1991

Mauger, Benig, *Songs from the Womb: Healing the Wounded Mother*, The Collins Press, Ireland, 1998

Patel, Dr Chandra, *The Complete Guide to Stress Management*, Macdonald Optima, UK, 1989

Peck, Scott, *The Road Less Travelled*, Rider, UK, 1997

Ray, Sondra and Mandel, Bob, *Birth and Relationships: How Your Birth Affects Your Relationships*, Celestial Arts, CA, 1987

Rosenberg, Jack *et al*, *Body, Self and Soul: Sustaining Integration*, Humanics Ltd, US, 1991

Saunders, Alex, *et al*, *It Hurts Me Too: Children's Experiences of Domestic Violence*, Saunders, WAFF, NISW, Childline, UK, 1995

Stevens, Jay, *Storming Heaven, LSD and the American Dream*, Paladin, UK, 1987

Stone, Hal and Stone, Sidra, *Embracing Ourselves: The Voice Dialogue Manual*, New World Library, CA, 1989

Taylor, Kylea, *The Breathwork Experience: Exploration and Healing in Non-ordinary States of Consciousness*, Hanford Mead, CA, 1994

Verny, Dr Thomas with Kelly, John, *The Secret Life of the Unborn Child*, Warner Books, UK 1981

Watts, Alan, *The Book: On the Taboo Against Knowing Who You Are*, Vintage Books, NY, 1966

Whitfield, Dr Charles L, *Co-Dependence: Healing the Human Condition*, Health Communications Inc., FA, 1991

Yalom, Irvin, *The Theory and Practice of Group Psychotherapy*, Basic Books Inc., NY, 1975

Useful Addresses

British Rebirth Society
6 Rokesby Street
Leamington
Newcastle NE15 8RR
Tel: 0191 264 7553

Rebirthing Association of Ireland
Catherine Dowling
33 Inchicore Road
Kilmainham
Dublin 8
Tel: (00 353) 1 453 3166

International Breathwork Foundation
101 Rue de Bosnie
B-1060 Bruxelles
Belgium
Tel: (00 32) 2 537 3395
Website: *www.ibfnetwork.org*

Australian Association of Professional Rebirthers
4 Wirth Place
Greenwith
SA 5125
Australia
Tel: (0061) 8 828 964 05

Transformation Incorporated
4200 West Good Hope
Milwaukee
WI 53209-2250
USA
Tel: (001) 414 351 5770

Perceptions International
3200 N. Federal Highway
Suite 105
Boca Raton
FL 33431
USA
Tel: (001) 561 361 0440

ARTI
PO Box 29566
Atlanta
GA 30359
USA

A list of member practitioners, national organisations and schools
of rebirthing throughout the world is available in directory form
from the International Breathwork Foundation.

Index

180

INDEX

PIATKUS BOOKS

If you have enjoyed reading this book, you may be interested in other titles published by Piatkus. These include:

After Long Silence: A woman's search for her family's secret identity Helen Fremont

Art As Medicine: Creating a therapy of the imagination Shaun McNiff

Art Of Sexual Magic, The: How to use sexual energy to transform your life Margo Anand

Beyond Belief: How to develop mystical consciousness and discover the God within Peter Spink

Care Of The Soul: How to add depth and meaning to your everyday life Thomas Moore

Children And The Spirit World: A book for bereaved families Linda Williamson

Companion to Grief: Finding consolation when someone you love has died Patricia Kelley

Confidence to Be Yourself, The Dr. Brian Roet

Expecting Adam: A true story of birth, transformation and unconditional love

Full Catastrophe Living: How to cope with stress, pain and illness using mindfulness meditation Jon Kabat-Zinn

Good News for Bad Days: Living a soulful life Father Paul Keenan

Healing Breakthroughs: How your attitudes and beliefs can affect your health Dr Larry Dossey

Healing Your Family Patterns: How to access the past to heal the present David Furlong

Hymns To An Unknown God: Awakening the spirit in everyday life Sam Keen

Hypnosis Brian Roet

I Ching *or* Book Of Changes, The: A guide to life's turning points Brian Browne Walker

Lao Tzu's Tae Te Ching Timothy Freke

Light Up Your Life: And discover your true purpose and potential Diana Cooper

Living Magically: A new vision of reality Gill Edwards

184

185

Piatkus are also proud to present our new Mind, Body and Spirit series. Each of these accessible and inspiring guides is written by an expert in the field. Titles include: **Meditation**, **Celtic Wisdom**, **Tarot**, **The Essential Nostradamus**, **Feng Shui**, and **Crystal Wisdom**, **Reiki**, **Psychic Awareness**, **Colour Healing** and **Kabbalah**. Forthcoming titles include: **Angels**, **Shamanism**, **Astrology**, **Earth Mysteries**, **Druidry**, **Karma and Reincarnation**, **Pendulum Dowsing**, **Native American Wisdom** and **Palmistry**. These beautifully designed, in-depth introductions cost only £5.99.

For a free brochure with our complete list of titles, please write to:
Piatkus Books

5 Windmill Street
London W1P 1HF

Tel: 020 7631 0710
E-mail: info@piatkus.co.uk
Website: www.piatkus.co.uk